STARGAZING

FROM GAME RESERVES
in Southern Africa

ANTHONY FAIRALL

Illustrations by Margie Walter
Artwork by Angela Key

DEDICATION
To Alex

Published by Struik Nature
(an imprint of Penguin Random House SA
(Pty) Ltd)
Reg. No. 1953/000441/07
The Estuaries No. 4, Oxbow Crescent,
Century Avenue, Century City, 7441
PO Box 1144, Cape Town, 8000
South Africa

Visit www.penguinrandomhouse.co.za
and join the Struik Nature Club
for updates, news, events
and special offers.

10 9 8 7

Publishing manager: **Pippa Parker**
Managing editor: **Lynda Ingham-Brown**
Editor: **Pierra Abott**
Project manager: **Cisca Vennard**
Designer: **Robin Cox**
Cartographer: **Margie Walter**
Artwork: **Angela Key**
Proofreader: **Joanna Ward**
Indexer: **Cora Ovens**

Reproduction by
Hirt & Carter Cape (Pty) Ltd
Printed and bound in China by Leo Paper
Products Ltd.

ISBN: 9781770072152 (PRINT)
ISBN: 9781920572327 (EPUB)
ISBN: 9781920572334 (PDF)

Picture credits:

Animal artwork at start of chapters by
Angela Key, P.O. Box 465, Onrusriver 7201.
All maps and explanatory diagrams designed
by the author and drawn by Margie Walter,
Iziko Planetarium.
Enhanced Milky Way (page 15) from Axel
Mellinger, University of Potsdam.
Colour photography on pages 6, 16, 22, 23,
24, 29, 34, 38, 41, 42 and 57 from Prof.
Michael Bessell (Australian National
University) with Michelle Buxton, Bob
Watson, John Shobbrook, Paul Price, Ken
Hargreaves, Ralph Sutherland, Hwankyung
Sung and students from the Universities of
Sydney, New South Wales and Wollongong.
Front cover: Shane Doyle - The Media Bank/
africanpictures.net, Albert Jansen (stars)
Title page: Kim Thunder / africanpictures.net
Black and white images on pages 22, 29, 33,
37 and 40 courtesy of the UK Schmidt
Telescope (copyright in which is owned by
the Particle Physics and Astronomy Research
Council of the UK and the Anglo-Australian
Telescope Board) and the Digitized Sky
Survey created by the Space Telescope
Science Institute, operated by AURA, Inc, for
NASA, and is reproduced here with permis-
sion from the Royal Observatory Edinburgh.
Colour photographs on pages 5, 7, 12, 50,
51, 54, 55 and 70 from NASA.

Special thanks to the family of the late Albert Jansen
for the use of the background star image on the
cover, title, imprint and contents pages.

CONTENTS

INTRODUCTION
WHY STARGAZE FROM GAME RESERVES?

Numerous pairs of luminous eyes shine back in the light of my headlamp. I am standing outside a rest hut in Umfolozi. The winter night has fallen early and a herd of impala have bedded down beneath the nearby trees, unperturbed by the roving hyena that earlier made off with the lamb chops by the braaivleis fire. The eyes of the impala look like stars, and for a moment the stars above seem like staring eyes. I extinguish the headlamp as my gaze travels upward. There is the centre of the great city of stars in which we live. Rarely can one see it so clearly. The power generator has been turned off and not a single artificial light is in sight. After a day immersed in the beauty of the natural world, there is no reason to stop just because the sun has set. A game reserve is not only ideal for viewing animals but also the ideal location from which to view stars.

The best way of seeing stars is to go somewhere where there is as little artificial light as possible. Game reserves provide the perfect setting.

In centuries past it was not necessary to go to game reserves to see animals, or to see stars. In van Riebeeck's time, lion, elephant and other big game abounded in the Cape Peninsula, let alone the rest of the subcontinent. For example, Franschhoek Pass – only an hour's drive from Cape Town – was originally an elephant trail. (Elephants, like humans, sought the easiest and most sensible routes in crossing mountain ranges.) Sadly, widespread hunting destroyed their paradise. The establishment of farms and the development of towns and cities drove away the remaining animals until only pockets of the natural world were left, the game reserves of today.

Strangely enough, the same is true of stars. It seems odd, because you only have to look upwards to see the night sky, regardless of where you are situated on the surface of the Earth. Indeed, up until the 1960s that was true. Many enthusiastic amateur astronomers set up telescopes in their own backyards, and professional observatories operated in major cities. Both Cape Town and Johannesburg have suburbs named 'Observatory', after the institutions they hosted.

LIGHT POLLUTION

Over the past few decades, however, the stars appear to have dimmed with advances in technology having resulted in much more efficient ways of generating light. Outdoor lighting, in particular street lighting and 'security' lighting, has become a ubiquitous feature of suburbia. Today sporting events are regularly held at night, something that was not possible years ago. We have the technology to generate enormous amounts of bright light, and we do. The problem with such light is that it not only illuminates the ground below, but also the atmosphere above. Astronomers were the first to become aware of this.

Even in cities, it used to be possible to see stars against a black sky. However, when the sky is no longer black, but grey, it is more difficult to see the fainter stars. Astronomers found it increasingly impractical to work from city observatories. Since the 1960s, cities have grown larger and more populous, and their light output has increased immensely. Fortunately, city engineers have realised that light that shines straight up into the sky is wasted light, and thus wasted electricity, and they have designed more effective light fittings to cut down on 'light pollution'. However, we can only see the brighter stars from the cities.

WHY STARGAZE FROM GAME RESERVES?

The best way of seeing stars is to go somewhere where there is as little artificial light as possible. Large stretches of the Karoo are one possibility. That is where we astronomers migrate when we want to study the stars nowadays, but, as an amateur, unless you are extremely dedicated, you are unlikely to make a special journey to the Karoo. Game reserves, which have very little artificial lighting are ideal for stargazing.

In general, South African winters provide fine and clear weather, and these are the perfect conditions for stargazing. If you are visiting a game reserve in this season (or any other for that matter) you are likely to be carrying warm clothes, a torch and a pair of binoculars for gameviewing by day and these should prove to be just as useful during your 'game' viewing

activities at night. Before you charge on and skip to the chapters covering the celestial 'Big Five', starting in Chapter 3 with the Southern Cross, spend some time on Chapter 1 to ensure that you get the most out of your stargazing experience.

Besides these practical factors, there is an even bigger reason why you should explore the night sky from a game reserve. The joy of game reserves is that you escape the office blocks, shopping malls, and traffic jams of busy city life. Game reserves provide time out and time to think. They afford us a chance to explore the natural world and appreciate our planet and its multitude of fauna and flora.

Game viewing is the experience of exploring the natural world, looking around us. Stargazing is also exposure to the natural world, but in this case it is looking up.

Both these experiences provide an opportunity to recharge the soul.

The whole African continent has less light pollution than Europe. The light pollution that does exist is concentrated in the cities, making game reserves ideal for stargazing.

CHAPTER 1
THE RIGHT CONDITIONS

When preparing to spend an evening under the stars, make sure that the conditions are right. Ideally, there should be no moon or clouds in the sky, although even a sliver of moon and partially cloudy weather might still yield some good sightings. This chapter explains how to use your binoculars and the star maps, which appear in the back of the book, as well as the technique for adapting your eyes to the dark.

WEATHER

Most game reserves in southern Africa experience rainfall in summer, when the cloudy 'Intertropical Convergence Zone' migrates southwards with the Sun, carrying moist air that feeds the turbulent thunderstorms. By contrast, winters are dry with fine clear weather, save for the occasional cold front from the Cape. Summers can also be sticky and hot, so most visitors prefer to visit game reserves in the cooler months. The clear skies experienced during these months are the inspiration for this little book, and are as fine as any you could experience on Earth. These clear nights, without any of the artificial light found in towns and cities, recall what darkest Africa must have been like not so long ago.

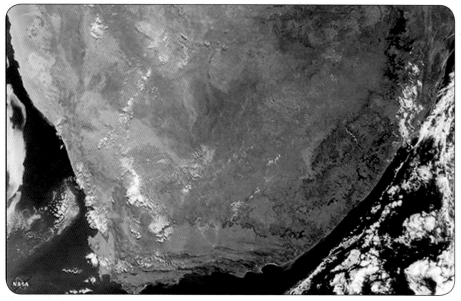

In winter there is usually relatively little cloud cover over the sub-continent.

During the winter months, at least four out of five nights are clear over the central and western interior of southern Africa. The chance of cloudy weather increases mildly towards the east coast; only the Cape experiences 50% cloud cover on average during winter.

Partly cloudy weather is not as much of a problem in a game reserve as in a city. In a city the undersides of the clouds are lit up by the city lights, making it difficult to see the stars in the clear gaps. In the absence of artificial lighting, clouds seen from game reserves are conveniently black. Sometimes it is only the absence of stars in the sky that reveal the presence of clouds. A few scattered clouds, though undesirable, are therefore not a complete disaster.

BEWARE THE MOON

The Moon may be a problem as it can cause just as much light pollution as city lights (not the whole Moon, mind, only the portion lit by sunlight). Like the Earth, the Moon is a spherical body, and half of its surface is lit up by sunshine (the day side), while the other half remains in shadow (the night side). The problem is that when we experience night-time, a sizable part of the Moon may still be lit up by the Sun. That part dazzles our eyes and prevents them from becoming properly adapted to the dark. The Moon is dark grey in colour and reflects only 6% of the sunlight, but even that is still far too much. The best time for stargazing is when there is no Moon in the night sky. There is an even chance of that happening, since the Moon can be below the horizon just as often as it can be above. Unfortunately, when it is above the horizon at night, there is usually a greater portion illuminated by sunlight.

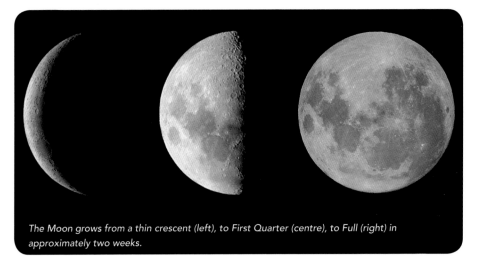

The Moon grows from a thin crescent (left), to First Quarter (centre), to Full (right) in approximately two weeks.

VISIBILITY AND PHASES

The Moon completes its cycle – New Moon to New Moon – in 29.5 days (the basis for a calendar month). When the Moon first reappears in the evening sky, following New Moon, it is seen as a thin crescent in the west. The thin crescent is the only portion of the Moon's spherical surface we can see lit up by sunlight; almost all the sunlight is falling on the other side of the Moon. This is a good time for stargazing, as the thin crescent does not produce enough light to 'pollute' the night sky. And, in any case, the Moon sets very early. Even on the nights after it first appears, the Moon is not a big problem. However, the sliver of a crescent is growing fatter and by the time the Moon is close to First Quarter, it is a problem. The 'Quarter' refers to how far the Moon has advanced in its orbit and to its cycle of phases, and not to how much of it is seen illuminated. During First Quarter, one half of its visible side is illuminated by sunlight (its day side) and one half is in its own shadow (its night side). It is already producing enough moonlight to enable you to see where you are going when walking through the bush at night. This is bad news for stargazing.

And then things get worse. In the week following First Quarter, the Moon waxes (grows) to Full Moon. A Full Moon is a splendid, romantic sight, but it is absolutely lousy for stargazing. There might as well be street lighting over the whole game reserve. Our eyes struggle to become dark adapted. Heavy cloud cover would block out the Moon, but unfortunately the stars would be blocked out as well. In short, if the Moon is near full, don't waste your time stargazing, as you will only be disappointed.

Fortunately, every night after Full Moon the Moon rises later and later; on average almost an hour later every night. It is therefore best to stargaze before the Moon rises. However, after a few nights the problem will have vanished: for the rest of its orbit – up to Last Quarter and back to New Moon – the Moon is visible only during the early morning.

In short, as the Moon goes through its 29.5-day cycle of phases, about 11 days (from just before First Quarter) are a problem for evening stargazing. Use the table below as a guide to optimum dates.

	2022	2023	2024	2025	2026	2027	2028	2029	2030	2031	2032	2033	2034	2035	2036
Jan	17	6	25	13	3	22	12	30	19	8	27	15	4	23	13
Feb	16	5	24	12	1	20	10	28	18	7	26	14	3	22	11
Mar	18	7	25	14	3	22	11	30	19	9	27	16	5	23	12
Apr	16	6	23	13	2	20	9	28	18	7	25	14	3	22	10
May	16	5	23	12	1/31	20	8	27	17	7	25	14	3	22	10
Jun	14	4	22	11	29	19	7	26	15	5	23	12	2	20	8
Jul	13	3	21	10	29	18	6	25	15	4	22	12	1/31	20	8
Aug	12	1/31	19	9	28	17	5	24	13	3	21	10	29	19	7
Sep	10	29	18	7	26	15	3	22	11	1/30	19	9	28	17	5
Oct	9	28	17	7	26	15	3	22	11	30	18	8	27	17	5
Nov	8	27	15	5	24	14	2	21	10	28	17	6	25	15	4
Dec	8	27	15	4	24	13	2/31	20	9	28	16	6	25	15	3

This table shows the dates of Full Moon every year until 2036. It is best to avoid stargazing in the evening from about eight days before to three days after Full Moon.

THE HUMAN EYE

Humans, like apes, have forward-facing eyes. This arrangement provides stereoscopic vision, which is excellent for judging nearby distances when moving from rock to rock (or branch to branch), but obviously not essential for stargazing. In addition, our eyes are adapted to seeing in the daytime, not at night: long before we jumped into our four-by-fours and headed for the game reserves, we existed as hunter-gatherers. Like the majority of the Earth's inhabitants, we chose to be active by day and to sleep at night. Most of us still function in this way and the adaptation of our eyesight to daytime use means that we do not see so well at night.

Suffice to say that, without artificial lighting, we cannot see well enough to walk around safely on a dark night. Owls and members of the cat family, on the other hand, can see quite well at night. The problem with our eyes is that they are not big enough. Even when the pupils dilate, they do not let enough light in. On the positive side, however, we have developed *night vision*. Night vision involves a different set of receptors in the retina of the eye. For day vision, we use *cone* receptors. Cones respond rapidly to movement and come in three types, each sensitive to a different colour – hence colour vision. They are particularly concentrated in a central spot, which means our eyes record what we are directly looking at in the greatest detail. For night vision, however, we utilise *rod* receptors. Rods are slower in response but more sensitive to light. They do not see colour and are not packed closely in any place, in fact they are absent from the central spot. Rods enable us to see in the dark, but only in black and white, and not with any sharp detail.

Before the rods can be used, the eye has to become dark adapted. This occurs when the chemical rhodopsin in the retina of the eye is dispersed. It takes about 40 minutes for our vision to become fully dark adapted from broad daylight, and much shorter from artificial lighting. Give yourself several minutes in darkened surroundings and you will be almost dark adapted. When you are, and you want to look at something very faint, look *a little to the side* of the object you want to see, so that its image falls outside the central spot (remember, there are no rods there). Astronomers are familiar with this trick of 'averted vision', which uses the rods in the eyes and not the cones.

Although many of us regard the night sky as something of great beauty, our eyes are in fact poorly equipped to really appreciate it fully. At best our eyes enable us to garner a shallow view of the Universe around us. The best remedy is to use a pair of binoculars – and most visitors to game reserves have a pair.

BINOCULARS

Keeping a pair of binoculars at hand to see more details of the animals usually enhances your enjoyment of a game reserve. You become adept at aiming and adjusting them. The open lenses of binoculars are much larger than the dilated pupils of the eye, and they work like funnels to direct much more light through those pupils. The result is that the eye can see much fainter objects more clearly. Try using your binoculars at night, and you can make out details of plants and perhaps animals in what seemed to the naked eye to be deep dark shadows. They can also improve your eyesight when looking at the night sky.

Binoculars are ideal for exploring the night sky, more so than telescopes. Telescopes are usually difficult to aim and handle, whereas binoculars are far more comfortable. For anyone starting out in astronomy – or only wanting to dip in their big toe – binoculars are ideal, and they are as effective in the night sky as they are for viewing game in the reserve.

The larger the front lenses of the binoculars, the better they are to see faint objects. Even 25 mm lenses will greatly improve your eyesight. The ideal is 50 mm lenses, as anything larger is usually too heavy to hold for sustained periods. Binoculars that

A pair of 7 X 50 binoculars. The '50' indicates the 50 mm aperture of the front lenses and the '7' means that they magnify objects seven times.

magnify seven to ten times are fine; anything more and you will need very steady hands. Magnification is not really as important for stargazing as it is for looking at animals. Aiming binoculars at a Nyala will conjure it up in greater detail. However, if you aim your binoculars at a pinpoint star it will still reveal nothing more than a pinpoint star (even expensive, giant telescopes cannot do better). A telescope may make them appear brighter, but not bigger. The only time telescopes come into their own is when we look at the Moon, the planets of our solar system and certain 'specialised' objects, such as double stars and small nebulae.

Be sure to set the binoculars so that they are properly focused for your eyes. Shut the right eye and use the knurled knob to achieve a sharp focus for the left eye. Then shut the left eye and rotate the right-hand eyepiece until it is comfortably focused. Set the separation of the eyepieces to match the spacing of your eyes. If possible, whether looking at animals or stars, each person should have his or her own pair of binoculars so that it remains optimally adjusted.

MAPS AND TORCHES

Other factors also contribute to the suitability of game reserves for stargazing. Since game viewing often starts in the early morning when there is a bit of a chill in the air, you are likely to have a warm jacket. That will also come in useful under the night sky. You are also likely to have a flashlight, which can be used to read the maps in this book.

The detailed maps will help you find various objects in the sky. Obviously you will not be able to read them in total darkness, but you should use only soft illumination so as not to spoil your dark adaptation.

If your torch is too bright, cover it with your hand and only allow a small amount of light to spill out. A red light is ideal, as it does not destroy night vision. For ease of reading, most of the detailed maps in this book show the stars as black dots against a white background.

HOW TO USE THE CONSTELLATION KEY

Not all constellations described in this book are visible at the same time. Whether or not a particular constellation or star is visible in the night sky depends on the time of year and the time of night at which you are stargazing.

To help you along (and to avoid wasting time looking for constellations that will not be visible), the introductions to Chapters Three to Eight indicate the months of the year in which the particular constellation or star, covered in that chapter, is in view. This information is summarised in an easy-to-use grid on the bottom left-hand corner of even-numbered pages.

The months in which a constellation is visible are highlighted in the grid. As in the example below, the constellation key indicates that the object will be visible from February to September. So, should you be stargazing between October and January, you would know to skip that particular chapter and to move on to a relevant one immediately.

18 J F M A M J J A S O N D

Evening visibility indicated from February to September by a constellation key diagram

CHAPTER 2
A CITY OF STARS

Even in a game reserve there is a bustling, expansive 'city' that we cannot escape – it is the city in which we all live; the city of stars, that is. We call this city of stars our Galaxy and this chapter will give you an idea of what you should be seeing when you venture into the dark southern African night.

There are about a million million stars in our Galaxy, and in places it gets very crowded. This is not the case where we live, however, because we are nowhere near the centre of this 'city'.

Our Galaxy is shaped like a great, flattened disc surrounding a central bulge (almost the way suburbs here on Earth surround high-rise city centres). We have never seen it from the outside, but we think it resembles the accompanying illustration. The central bulge is packed with billions of stars. The surrounding disc has a spiral structure and individual spiral arms are highlighted by super-bright stars, relatively few in number. That is where we live, between two dominant spiral arms: the Sagittarius Arm (closer to the centre) and the Perseus Arm (in a weaker spiral fragment or spur known as the Local or Orion Arm). The spiral pattern correctly suggests that the whole disc

Our Galaxy, flat on and edge on

is spinning, the inner part going around faster than the outside. It takes a couple of hundred million years for our Solar System to go once around the Galaxy.

The reason it takes so long is because the Galaxy is huge. It is said to be around 100 000 light years across, which means that is how long it would take a ray of light – which could get to the Moon in little more than a second – to travel from one side of the Galaxy to the other. We live a mere 25 000 light years from the centre! (The light year is a convenient and practical way of expressing vast astronomical distances. It is the distance that light can travel in one year, which is about 10 trillion km or 6.2 trillion miles.)

OUR CLOSEST STAR

Understanding that one lives in such a large galaxy is the first key point to absorb. The second is that the nearest of all the stars in the Galaxy is the Sun!

Seen up close, a star is an enormous spherical ball of incandescent gas. Stars are therefore round, not spiky, as they are commonly (however misleadingly) portrayed. Stars are also so massive that ongoing nuclear reactions occur in their cores, thereby generating and sustaining the energy that keeps them shining. The stars in the night sky are all suns, even though they look so puny compared to our Sun. The reason for this is because they are such enormous distances away, so much so that we cannot perceive their sizes at all, even with the help of a telescope. In fact, most of the stars we see in the night sky are bigger and brighter than our Sun. A few rare superluminous stars are even up to a million times brighter; others are several hundred times bigger. Such is the scale of the Galaxy, however, that we see them only as pinpoints.

The reason the Sun seems so much brighter is because we are so much closer to it, Earth being one of the eight major planets that orbit around the Sun. Given that our Earth is only three millionths of the Sun's mass, it is easy to understand why it did not achieve stardom. Just as well though – we need Earth as a place to live, and the Sun as our source of warmth and energy. This arrangement is akin to lighting a campfire at night and then arranging a chair beside it; not too close as to be too hot, and not so far as to be too cold.

So, when you gaze up at the night sky, think of those stars as distant campfires. Who knows what (or who) is sitting around them. It is believed that most stars have planets circling around them, just like our Solar System. So far, almost 200 other planets have been discovered out there, but they are far too faint to be visible to the naked eye.

THE MILKY WAY

Although there are a million million stars in our Galaxy, the dark-adapted naked eye can only see several thousand. The use of binoculars might push this number up to tens of thousands. The stars we do see individually are either of modest luminosity (but still somewhat brighter than our Sun) and very nearby, or super luminous (tens of thousands of times brighter than our Sun). The rest of the stars in the Galaxy are either too far away, or too dim or obscured by foreground dust clouds, to be seen individually. However, we can see them collectively. It is much like looking from afar towards a city at night: although we cannot see individual streetlamps, we do see the combined glow of the light they produce. So, too, are we able to see the glow of billions and billions of stars in our Galaxy. The light from those stars forms a luminous band that encircles us. We call this band the Milky Way.

On winter evenings the Milky Way stretches high above our heads, and we can look directly towards the centre of our Galaxy. The centre is not as obvious as one might expect, for an array of foreground dust clouds block much of the view. The centre itself is not visible, but a part of the central bulge is, as a faint patch of light; the light from billions of stars that has taken 25 000 years to travel towards us. We therefore see this light not as it is, but as it was 25 000 years ago. For a mighty city of stars, the Galaxy appears nowhere near as bright or as impressive as it ought to be, but that is because of our eyesight. Binoculars improve matters greatly, revealing countless stars, clusters of stars, occasional glowing patches of interstellar gas, and dark dust clouds, seen in silhouette. It has to be one of the most amazing sights in nature.

On summer evenings we gaze in the opposite direction, away from the centre, towards the edge of the Galaxy. We still see the Milky Way, but it is less impressive, as we are looking towards the outer regions of our city of stars.

In general, the glow of the Milky Way comes from stars several thousand light years distant; individual points of light from stars tens or hundreds of light years away. These far-away objects account for almost everything we see in the night sky. However, a few of the objects we see are not as far away, such as five of the major planets in our solar system (only light minutes or a light hour or so away). As long as they are not seen too close to the Sun, those east of the Sun are visible in the evening sky, those west of the Sun in the morning sky. Even nearby planets are too distant to be seen as discs; instead they look like very bright stars. One of them – Venus – is sometimes bright enough to be visible in the daytime (more about that in Chapter 9).

Closer still than the planets is, of course, the Moon, which is just over a light second away. And even closer are artificial satellites and shooting 'stars'. During the early evening and again before dawn, artificial satellites may appear, looking like moving stars and taking a couple of minutes to cross the sky. We see them because they are high enough to be in sunlight, while we are in the Earth's shadow. If they suddenly fade away, it is because they have passed into the shadow. Shooting 'stars', on the other hand, are usually tiny pebbles from interplanetary space on a collision course with the Earth, which are incinerated in the atmosphere about a hundred kilometres up.

Finally, the obvious: we can look up to see the night sky, but not down because the Earth is beneath our feet. The only way we would be able to see what is on the other side of the Earth is if we could somehow be floating far off in space. In short, not being able to look down prevents us from seeing half the sky. Although what we can see in the night sky changes with the time of night and the time of year, there is a small part of the sky we never get to see from southern Africa. As compensation, though, there is also a small part of the sky that we can always see that never sets below the horizon.

The remaining chapters focus on particular parts of the sky, and particular things to look at. At certain times of the year some of these will be above the horizon, and some will not, but there will always be a constellation to view if the conditions are right.

Happy stargazing!

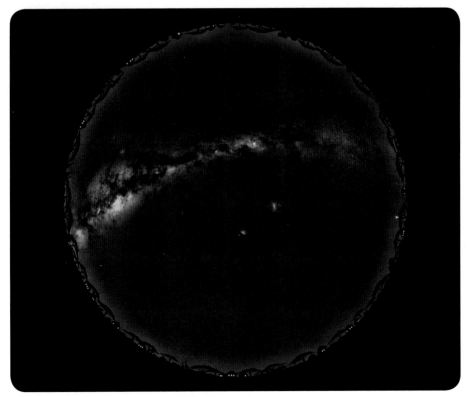

Axel Mellinger's enhanced view of the Milky Way crossing the night sky shows us our city of stars as seen from within.

CHAPTER 3
THE SOUTHERN CROSS

We set off on a stargazing safari to track down the celestial 'Big Five', starting in this chapter with the Southern Cross. Keep in mind that this constellation cannot be viewed throughout the year. Skip this chapter from October to January as the Southern Cross will be too low in the evening sky during this period (and even below the horizon from some parts of southern Africa).

FINDING THE SOUTHERN CROSS

If you are not familiar with finding star patterns, identifying the Southern Cross is a good way to start. The Cross itself is an easily recognisable pattern, almost as symmetrical as a man-made cross. The national flags of Australia and New Zealand display the Southern Cross; its shape is similar to that of the Christian cross. It is of course the human brain that constructs a pattern of four stars into a cross; it might actually be better described as a kite. Such interpretations are quite subjective: one of the stars is relatively faint and African people, for instance, saw it as a triangle of three bright stars.

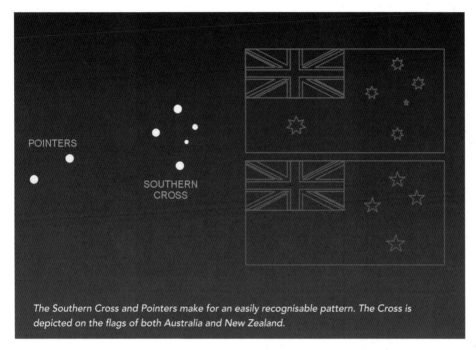

The Southern Cross and Pointers make for an easily recognisable pattern. The Cross is depicted on the flags of both Australia and New Zealand.

THE POINTERS

Next to the Cross is a pair of very bright stars, the Pointers. When the Cross is upright the Pointers are on its left. Together, these six stars – some of the brightest in the sky – form a distinctive enough 'asterism' to hunt down.

Take note, however, that the Cross may not always be upright and the Pointers to its left. The illustration on page 18 shows that when the Cross is high in the sky, it stands upright (with the Pointers to the left); when it is halfway up it lies on its side (with the Pointers above or below) and when it is almost at ground level it is upside down (with the Pointers to the right). More likely (in much the same way as the Grand Old Duke of York's ten thousand men) it will be neither up nor down. Imagine a gigantic clock face, where the Cross is fixed to the end of a hand that takes about 24 hours to go once around. The time of year as well as the time of night will determine the direction in which the 'clock hand' is pointing. Assuming you are stargazing in the evening, around 9 p.m., the illustration overleaf will help you determine which way up it is likely to be.

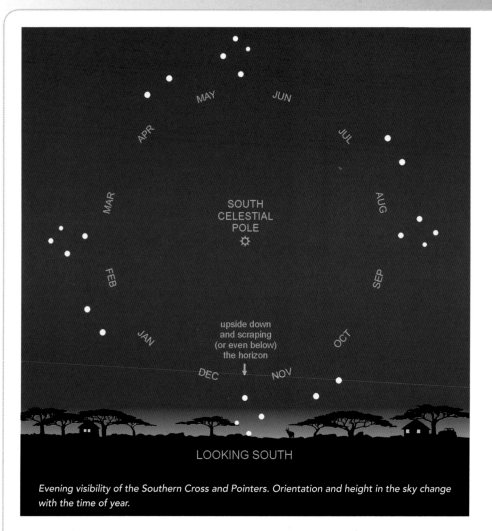

Evening visibility of the Southern Cross and Pointers. Orientation and height in the sky change with the time of year.

STILL HAVING TROUBLE LOCATING THE CROSS?

The instructions on page 17 should be sufficient even if this is the first time that you are looking for the Cross. However, if you're still battling, you are most likely expecting something much bigger or much smaller. There is a simple way of representing angular sizes in the sky. Hold a hand out at arm's length and bring three of your fingers together. The Cross ought to be about three fingers-width high and the Pointers about two and a bit fingers apart. That should give you a better idea of the size to expect. The other reason why you may not have found the Cross could be that it is low down in the sky and hidden by foreground trees or hills (or cloud). Remember the cautionary note at the very start of this chapter: do not try to find the Southern Cross during October to January, when it is too low in the sky. Finally, there is always a chance that it may be obscured by a bit of cloud. Try again on another occasion!

BEWARE THE 'FALSE CROSS'

If you think you have found the Cross but it has no accompanying Pointer stars, you have not found the genuine article: you have probably located a similar pattern, known for obvious reasons as the 'False Cross'.

This false cross lies quite close to the genuine Southern Cross, and, although it can cause some confusion, the real thing is not too far away from it. So you shouldn't be disheartened ... You are getting close.

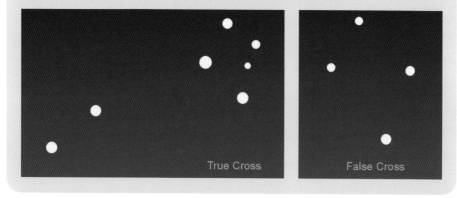

True Cross   False Cross

Officially, the Southern Cross is a separate constellation (the smallest of the 88) named 'Crux', Latin for cross. The individual stars within each constellation are named after letters in the Greek alphabet, with Alpha designating the brightest star, Beta the next brightest, and so on. (In this book they will be written as words, and not as Greek symbols.)

PICTURES IN THE SKY

The Sotho, Tswana and Venda saw the Pointers and the two brightest stars in the Cross as a group of four giraffes. The /Xam imagined the Pointers as two male lions, and the three brightest stars of the Cross as lionesses. The ancient Greeks imagined the two Pointer stars as part of a pattern representing a centaur – a creature half human, half horse.

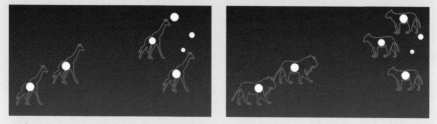

Indigenous representations of the Southern Cross

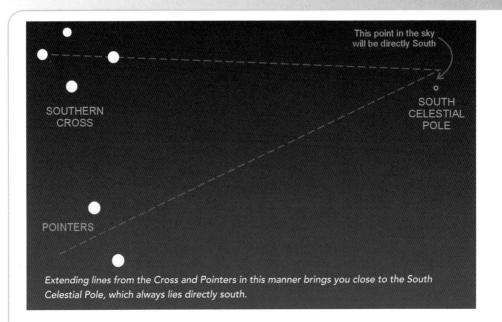

Extending lines from the Cross and Pointers in this manner brings you close to the South Celestial Pole, which always lies directly south.

How to find South with the Southern Cross

The accompanying diagram shows how to extend the axis of the Cross, like the tail of a kite, and then intersect it with a line bisecting the Pointers. The point where the lines intersect is very close to the South Celestial Pole where the axis of the Earth points into the southern sky. This Pole is visible from anywhere in the Southern Hemisphere and lies directly south.

An alternative 'recipe' is to extend the axis of the Cross, as in the diagram, by an extra four-and-a-half times the 'height' of the cross. This brings one to the same point.

Taking a closer look

Part of the beauty of this region is that the Pointers and Southern Cross are seen against the luminous band of the Milky Way, the brightest part of which lies just to the side of the Cross, on the opposite side of where the Pointers are. A general scan with binoculars should whet the appetite. Start at the Pointers, move towards the Cross, and then keep going. Many stars, clusters of stars great and small, and even a glowing 'nebula' should pass through your view. All this is part of the city of stars in which we live. The following are stops of interest on our tour of this city. Some of them will appear quite faint to the naked eye; binoculars or even averted vision (see Chapter 1) will reveal more detail. Refer to the map on page 21.

Alpha Centauri

You will hardly need binoculars to spot the Pointer star furthest from the Cross; it is one of the brightest stars in the sky. After the Sun, Alpha Centauri is the nearest of all our stellar neighbours, about four-and-a-third light years away (about 50 million million kilometres). Light takes over four years to travel from this star to us. So you are not really seeing it as it is tonight, but rather as it was over four years ago.

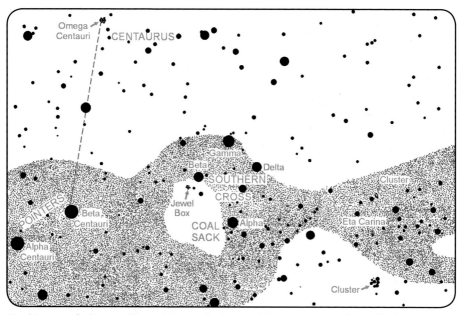

Use this map to find points of interest close to the Cross and Pointers. Stars are depicted as black dots.

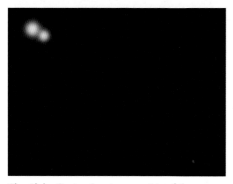

The Alpha Centauri system consists of three suns: Alpha Centauri A, Alpha Centauri B and Alpha Centauri C, which is too faint to be seen.

Alpha Centauri actually consists of two stars although this can only be shown by a telescope. Through a telescope, the system looks like the headlights of a distant car. One star is slightly brighter than the other, and that brighter star is exactly like our Sun. The two suns – Alpha Centauri A and Alpha Centauri B – take about 80 years to orbit around each other. A third sun in this system, Alpha Centauri C or Proxima Centauri, is quite far away from the other two and a bit nearer to Earth. It is so faint, however, (not even a ten thousandth of our Sun's luminosity) that it cannot be seen with the naked eye or with binoculars.

BETA CENTAURI

The other Pointer star, Beta Centauri, despite appearing to be a similar brightness to Alpha Centauri, is far more distant and luminous than its partner. Where Alpha Centauri is four light years away from Earth, Beta Centauri is a whopping 525 light years away! That means we see it as it appeared around the time that Christopher Columbus was about to set sail in the 1400s. Since it appears almost as bright as Alpha Centauri, it works out that this super-luminous star is approximately 14 000 times brighter than our Sun.

The Crux stars

The four bright stars of the Southern Cross are not at all as as close to us as Alpha Centauri, but not quite as distant as Beta Centauri. Alpha, Beta and Delta Crucis are all approximately 350 light years away, but Gamma Crucis is a mere 88 light years from Earth. Telescopes show Alpha Crucis to be a triple-star system, with two bright suns very close to each other and a fainter sun on the outside.

Omega Centauri

Omega Centauri is the king of all globular clusters, about a hundred of which dwell mainly around the central bulge of our galaxy. You will need to follow the map on page 21, since it can only just be seen with the naked eye. Follow a line from Alpha to Beta Centauri, then at Beta Centauri take a turn of 60 degrees to the left, which leads to a star. Keep going a bit further and you will find Omega Centauri. The naked eye should discern that whatever is there is not quite a star, but looking through binoculars will reveal something rather unexpected: a fuzzy ball of light. The light you are seeing is the combined light of almost a million stars, but at 17 500 light

Omega Centauri

years distant, they are much too far away to see individually. Globular clusters are very different to galactic clusters such as the Jewel Box (following below) . They have many more stars and are generally much more distant. The stars found in the clusters in our Galaxy must have formed a long time ago, and they are so massive that the cluster is held together by the gravitational pull of their member stars. While a galactic cluster might have hundreds or thousands of member stars, a globular cluster may have close to a million stars. Our Galaxy has about a hundred globu-lar clusters concentrated in a halo around its central bulge – the general direction in which we are now looking. Nevertheless, the two best examples of globular clusters are Omega Centauri and 47 Tucanae (page 41).

Jewel Box

This cluster of stars is situated very close to Beta Crucis, one of the four stars of the Southern Cross. It was a favourite of Sir John Herschel, who was one of the first to observe the southern skies with a powerful telescope from the Cape of Good Hope. He described it as a jewel box because of the different coloured stars one could see.

Jewel Box

Eta Carina region

Binoculars are best for viewing this region. Eta Carina is on the opposite side of the Southern Cross to the Pointers. There are a number of star clusters in its vicinity visible through binoculars, if not with the naked eye (refer to the map on page 21). You should find a patch of diffuse luminosity surrounding the star.

Eta Carina (close up)

The Milky Way is full of interstellar gas, but the gas is invariably cold, transparent and, like the air in front of your nose, quite invisible to the human eye.

There are a few isolated patches in which stars with extraordinarily high temperatures (so high that they emit ultraviolet radiation) excite the gas, causing it to glow. Eta Carina is a prime example of this phenomenon. In the nineteenth century it underwent an enormous eruption, and for a while it was the third brightest star in the night sky, in spite of its enormous distance of 7500 light years. Since then, it has faded to marginal naked-eye visibility.

Coal Sack

Not everything in our city of stars shines with light. Along the Milky Way numerous clouds of dust, dark and opaque, block our sight. One of the nearest – and undoubtedly the most famous – is the Coal Sack that appears to be pushed up against the Cross, although it is much more distant than the Cross. It can be seen in silhouette against the starry background either through binoculars or simply with the dark-adapted naked eye.

The Coal Sack (centre arrow) is seen immediately next to the Southern Cross. On the far right of the image is Eta Carina (right arrow).

CHAPTER 4
ORION

Orion is the second of the constellations to
track down. When we look in the direction of Orion on
summer evenings we are looking away from the centre
of the Galaxy. Orion is easily accessible between December
and April but at other times of the year it is likely
to be below the horizon during the evening.

Finding Orion

Orion is the most recognisable of all constellations. Its 'Belt' of three relatively bright stars, close to one another and arranged in an almost straight line, makes it easy to identify. The Belt is enclosed in an irregular four-sided box of four bright stars, two of which – Rigel and Betelgeuse – are amongst the brightest in the sky.

The bright stars of Orion

Almost all the visible stars in this constellation are super-luminous and very distant. Refer to the map overleaf. Rigel, the very bright white star, is so luminous that it could outshine our Sun 40 000 times. It is 773 light years away from Earth, which means that the light we now see left that star back in the thirteenth century.

Betelgeuse (which has been affectionately dubbed 'Beetlejuice') is 427 light years away from Earth. It is on the opposite side of the Belt from Rigel, and quite different from that star. The first obvious difference is the colour of the star – Betelgeuse is a reddish white as its surface temperature is cooler, making it red-hot instead of white-hot. What Betelgeuse lacks in temperature, however, it makes up for in size. It is a swollen 'red giant' star several hundred times the diameter of our Sun. If it were placed at the centre of our solar system, the Earth's orbit would lie inside it! Stars near the end of their lifetime become red giants like Betelgeuse. Our

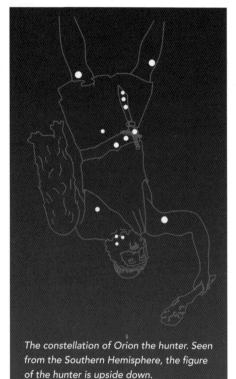

The constellation of Orion the hunter. Seen from the Southern Hemisphere, the figure of the hunter is upside down.

WEST ← WEST   LOOKING NORTH   EAST →

ww

Sun will eventually do the same; however, happily for us, that will only happen a few billion years from now.

The three stars of Orion's Belt are among the most distant stars that can be seen by the naked eye. Alnitak and Mintaka are at distances of 820 and 915 light years, respectively. Alnilam, the central star of the Belt, is an incredible 1 340 light years away; we see it today as it was around 670 AD, about the time that Britain was being introduced to Christianity. Its true luminosity must be getting on for a million times greater than that of the Sun. Being so bright, it burns fuel at a tremendous rate, and by stellar standards it has a very short lifetime, probably far less than a million years. Such stars die before they can leave the 'maternity home' where they were born. (Orion boasts such a region of star formation, the closest one to our solar system, which will be discussed later in this chapter.)

TAURUS

The map opposite shows some of the constellations in the neighbourhood of Orion. The first of these is Taurus (the Bull). Follow the line of Orion's Belt down and to the left (unless, towards April, Orion is already so low in the sky that this is impractical). Taurus differs from other constellations in that it is dominated by two 'galactic' clusters of stars, the two nearest clusters to our solar system. The most obvious of these is the Pleiades, also known in southern Africa as Isilimela. There is no other pattern in the night sky as compact as this group of stars, which is some 440 light years distant. Most of the other visible stars in Taurus belong to the second cluster, the Hyades, centred on an asterism that supposedly forms the face of the Bull. The brightest star, Aldebaran (which has a slightly reddish white colour), is a foreground object 65 light years away, while the cluster itself is 150 light years away.

Such clusters are common throughout our Galaxy. More distant examples can be seen through binoculars. The stars in the Pleiades are relatively young, as most stars are thought to form in clusters, not as isolated individuals. In time, however, the clusters disperse.

SIRIUS AND CANIS MAJOR

Follow the line of Orion's Belt up and to the right towards the brightest star in the night sky, Sirius. Unlike the super-luminnous distant stars in Orion, Sirius appears bright because it is one of our nearest stellar neighbours, not quite 9 light years away. It has about 23 times the luminosity of our Sun. Like Alpha Centauri (see page 20) it is a double star, of which one star has gone beyond the 'red giant' phase (as described with Betelgeuse in the discussion earlier in this

Map of Orion showing all the stars visible to the human eye.

Saiph
Rigel
Great Nebula
Alnitak
Alnilam
Mintaka
Bellatrix
Betelgeuse

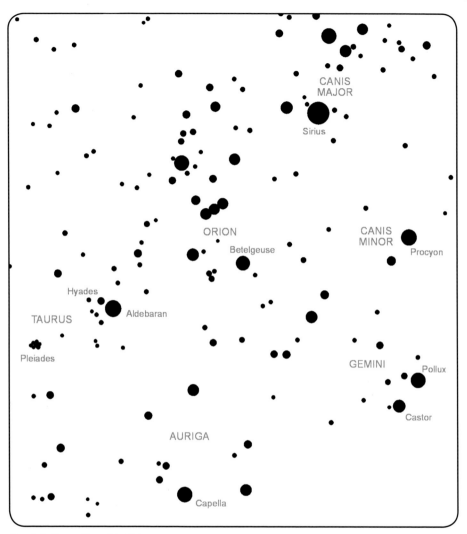

Constellations adjacent to Orion

chapter) and shed its outer layers back into space. Only the collapsed core of the original star remains; with fuel reserves exhausted, gravity has condensed it into a tiny dense 'white dwarf', not much bigger than our Earth. Yet it has a mass similar to that of our Sun, and a teaspoonful of its material would weigh 500 kg! It forms a very faint companion to the main star, and is lost in its glare. It is not visible either with the naked eye or through binoculars. The host constellation is Canis Major (Big Dog), which has a pattern of reasonably bright stars, as shown in the map. Sirius (sometimes called the 'dog star') marks the head, another the front paw, while the others group in a distinctive asterism, towards the dog's 'tail end'.

Gemini

If Orion is high in the sky, a line perpendicular to Orion's Belt extended downward past Betelgeuse will eventually lead to a pair of widely spaced bright stars. These are Castor and Pollux in the constellation of Gemini (the Twins). Castor is a remarkable multiple system with no less than six suns, but to the naked eye (and even through binoculars) it appears as a single star. It is 51 light years away. Pollux is 34 light years away.

Procyon and Canis Minor

Between Canis Major and Gemini we find the constellation Canis Minor (Little Dog) with a single bright star. Procyon, is only 11 light years away from Earth and the eighth brightest star in the sky.

Auriga

Lying between Taurus and Gemini is a distorted pentagon of stars, Auriga (the Charioteer). This constellation is visible above the northern horizon only when Orion is high in the sky. Its bright star is Capella, which is 43 light years distant. It also happens to be the sixth brightest star visible from Earth.

INDIGENOUS BELIEFS

The three stars of Orion's Belt – 'imPhambano' to the Zulu and 'amaRoza' to the Xhosa – were well known to the indigenous people of southern Africa. They were considered to depict three animals, usually warthogs. It is interesting that both the ancient Greeks and the people of southern Africa associated this constellation with hunting!

The Pleiades – Isilimela in Xhosa and Zulu – play an important role in African society. This cluster formed the main basis of the calendar conceived by the traditionally agrarian Xhosa and Zulu people. For several weeks around May, Isilimela is lost in the glare of the Sun and not visible in either the evening or the morning skies. Sometime in June (which is also called Isilimela in Xhosa) the cluster reappears in the morning twilight, a signal to start preparing the fields for a new agricultural year. It is for this reason that the Pleiades were dubbed the 'digging stars'. In Xhosa society the reappearance of these stars not only marked the beginning of the agricultural year, but also the time when boys underwent initiation; indeed, Xhosa men count their years of manhood as so many Isilimelas. As spring became summer and crops grew, Isilimela progressed from the morning to the evening sky, eventually fading into the evening twilight once harvesting was complete.

Looking through binoculars

Although the Milky Way – the Galaxy seen from within – passes close to Orion, it is relatively anaemic compared to what we see when we look in the other direction. Nevertheless, there are some interesting objects we can track down through binoculars.

PICTURES IN THE SKY

The ancient astronomers linked most of the constellations we have encountered thus far into a great hunting scene: Orion, the hunter, holds a club above his head as he engages the fierce bull, while his hunting dogs support him. Regrettably, seen from the Southern Hemisphere, the scene is upside down, as in the diagram on page 25.

The Khoisan's (or Bushmen's) interpretation – depicted on page 24 at the beginning of this chapter – tells of Aob the hunter (represented by the Hyades cluster) who was sent by his wives (the Pleiades) to shoot three zebra (Orion's Belt). Sadly, his arrow (Orion's scabbard) missed the zebra. Aob could not recover his arrow as a lion (Betelgeuse) was nearby. The zebra survived and eventually (when Orion sets below the horizon) escaped to Earth.

Orion has the brightest of the 'emission nebulae', which are glowing clouds of gas. The map on page 26 indicates how to find the 'Great Nebula' in Orion. The Great Nebula functions as a 'maternity home' for stars. At its heart is a tight bunch of four bright stars – they will appear as one star through binoculars – that emit sufficient ultraviolet radiation to cause the surrounding gas, mainly hydrogen, to glow.

The nebula lies within a more extensive dust cloud, thick and opaque enough to prevent us seeing through it. It is in fact a hollow cavity blown by newly formed stars. Condensations that will eventually become individual stars have formed in the surrounding dust (and gas) cloud. The Hubble Space Telescope has revealed that some embryonic stars and solar systems have already come into being. Because star formation takes millions of years we will not observe any changes, but will see stars at various stages of their early lives.

Another object that is suitable for viewing through binoculars is the Pleiades Cluster. The naked eye only manages to see six or seven stars. Binoculars may show twenty or more. Even so, these are but the brightest of some 500 stars believed to belong to the cluster. Also scan the Milky Way – especially alongside Canis Major – for fainter clusters.

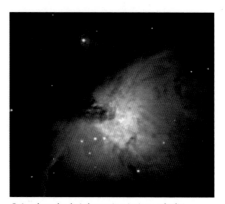

Orion has the brightest 'emission nebula' (glowing cloud of gas) in the sky.

The Pleiades cluster

Chapter 5
Leo

Appropriately, the lion is one of the big five constellations to track down. Like its terrestrial counterpart, it is not always immediately obvious and may take a little while to spot. Since it forms one of the constellations of the Zodiac, many readers will already know Leo by name, rather than by its pattern of stars. We can only go lion hunting from February to June, when Leo is above the horizon during the evening.

FINDING LEO

This constellation contains a distinctive sickle-shaped asterism and an almost perfect right-angled triangle, as shown below. Remember that the pattern in the sky will seem much larger than it seems in the figure. It is generally visible above the northern horizon, as suggested in the bottom image. If you experience trouble finding it, stretch an arm out and put three fingers together. Three finger widths are about half the size of the sickle pattern in Leo.

Regulus is the brightest star in Leo. It is 77 light years away, which means that we see it as it was around the time of the Great Depression.

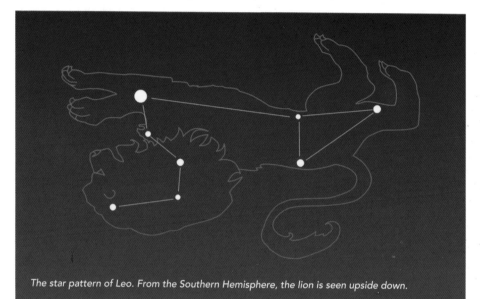

The star pattern of Leo. From the Southern Hemisphere, the lion is seen upside down.

← WEST   LOOKING NORTH   EAST →

The visibility of Leo in the evening sky

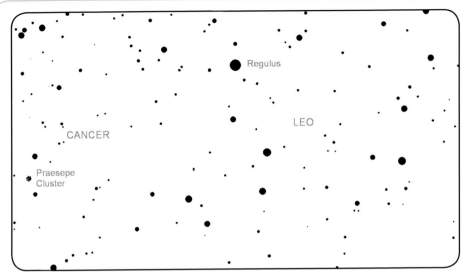

Stars (as faint as the eye can see) in Leo and neighbouring Cancer.

LEO AND THE ZODIAC

In modern times, we know Leo as a pattern of distant stars. However in ancient times, the pattern held a mystical nature, especially when the Sun 'god' interacted with it.

Leo is one of the well-known signs of the Zodiac or 'sun signs'. This is because Leo is in the band of sky through which the Sun appears to pass. 'Appears to pass' is optimistic, to say the least, when it is obviously impossible to see where the Sun is in relation to star patterns. However, the ancients would have noted which constellations first appeared where the Sun went down, and which constellations were last seen before the Sun came up. This would have enabled them to work out in which constellation the Sun lay. They may even have been able to see constellations during a total eclipse of the Sun, which would have helped them to pinpoint the position of the Sun more accurately.

In modern times, the Sun appears to pass through Leo from August 11 to September 17 (in the times of the ancient Babylonians, it would have been July 23 to August 24). If your birthday falls between those dates, then you were supposedly born 'under the sign of Leo' when the Sun 'god', the dominant influence, was interacting with Leo. Remarkably, modern astrologers still use the old dates rather than the current ones. Consequently, when they say the Sun is in Leo, more often than not the Sun is actually in Cancer! Suffice to say that modern astronomers do not see the Sun as a deity controlling our daily lives.

LOOKING THROUGH BINOCULARS

Leo is situated out of the plane of our Galaxy; consequently this portion of the sky is relatively bland when swept with binoculars. Nevertheless there is a beautiful cluster of stars to be found.

The constellation to the left of Leo is Cancer, another well-known sign of the Zodiac. Cancer is unlikely to feature among the 'big five' as its stars are very faint, with hardly any recognisable pattern. However, its redeeming feature is the Praesepe Cluster, a relatively nearby cluster (but not as near, nor as bright, as the Pleiades and the Hyades in Taurus. See Orion and company in Chapter 4). All its stars are too faint for the naked eye to see individually, but their combined light is just discernable if one uses averted vision (looking a little to the side with a dark-adapted eye). This cluster is 577 light years away and has at least 350 members. Binoculars will show only the very brightest of these.

The Praesepe Cluster

METEOR SHOWERS

Every year, in mid-November, the Earth passes near the debris of an old comet. This results in a shower of meteors, small particles seen for only a second or two as they burn up on entering our planet's atmosphere. The Leonids (so named because they seem to come from the direction of Leo) have, at certain times in history, produced spectacular showers. However, in November Leo and the Leonids are only visible in the early morning sky.

Leonids (left), as recorded by a camera, and – (right) somewhat exaggerated – by an artist.

CHAPTER 6
SCORPIUS

Scorpius too is a well-known constellation of the Zodiac.
Scorpius is the fourth of the big five constellations to
hunt. Read this chapter if it is May to October, as
Scorpius will then be in the evening sky. However,
if you haven't already explored the Southern Cross
region (Chapter 3), rather do that first.

FINDING SCORPIUS

Aside from the Southern Cross, Scorpius is the most recognisable constellation in the winter skies. Those who know the pattern will find it very easily, but for someone starting out it presents a challenge because it is not as simple as the Cross or Orion's Belt. The pattern, shown in the diagrams below, appears somewhat larger than your hand would, with fingers stretched apart and held at arm's length. If you can make out the line of the Milky Way, follow it from the Southern Cross, past the Pointers and it will lead to the tail end of Scorpius. The stars of Scorpius form a long curving line, for once resembling the creature they supposedly represent, from the 'pincers'

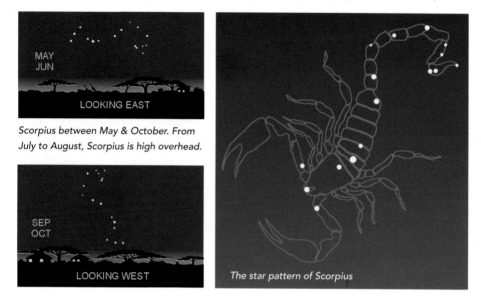

MAY
JUN

LOOKING EAST

Scorpius between May & October. From July to August, Scorpius is high overhead.

SEP
OCT

LOOKING WEST

The star pattern of Scorpius

right round to the curving tail and the sting at the end. The sting is represented by two stars located close together, part of an asterism that looks like a distorted cross, and is fairly easily recognised. The bright star Antares lies at the centre of the scorpion's body (see map overleaf). Its name implies that it is 'the rival of Mars' because of its reddish colour. However, Mars is a tiny planet while Antares is a giant star, probably 200 000 times greater in diameter! The difference is that Mars is usually only 5 to 20 light minutes away, but Antares is 604 light years distant – we see Antares today as it was at the beginning of the fifteenth century! Hence a small planet nearby can easily mimic a super-luminnous star far away.

SCORPIUS OR SCORPIO?

Most people know Scorpio as one of the signs of the Zodiac. More correctly it is an astrological 'sun sign' so that when the sun is in Scorpio in late October/early November, humans born around then are supposedly under its influence. Back in 500 BC Scorpio was one and the same as the constellation of Scorpius. That is no longer the case: today, the astrological Scorpio corresponds with the constellation of Libra, and the astronomical Scorpius with the astrological Sagittarius – further reason why modern science does not support astrological beliefs.

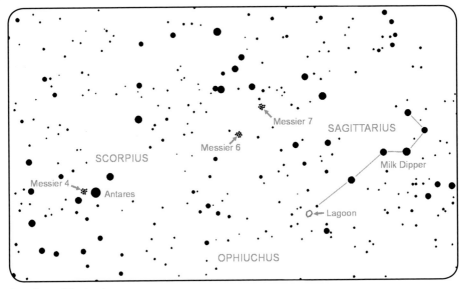

Scorpius and Sagittarius

PICTURES IN THE SKY

In Greek mythology the scorpion was sent by Gaia, goddess of the Earth, to bring about the downfall of the boastful hunter, Orion, who had threatened to wipe out all the animals of Earth. Orion, with his head held high, never spotted the small but deadly creature until it was too late. The constellations of Orion and Scorpius lie on opposite sides of the sky, so when Orion sinks, mortally wounded, to the western horizon, Scorpius rises victoriously in the east. The story has a happy ending for Orion, who was saved by Ophiuchus, the doctor of antiquity, whose constellation follows Scorpius.

SAGITTARIUS

The jumble of brightish stars that follow the tail of Scorpius form Sagittarius, the Archer. It would take considerable imagination to picture a centaur – half human, half horse – complete with bow and arrow. The pattern of stars in Sagittarius does not lend itself to easy recognition, except perhaps for a small asterism known as the Milk Dipper (vaguely resembling the Big Dipper in the northern skies).

THE MILKY WAY

Scorpius and Sagittarius lie across the luminous band of the Milky Way, the city of stars in which we live. When we look in their direction, we are looking towards the centre of our Galaxy. From July to September, when these two constellations are high in the evening sky, one needs to look with eyes that are dark adapted (and there should be no Moon or clouds in the sky). The view that we see is arguably one of the greatest sights in Nature, possibly the most rewarding astronomical memory of a game reserve visit.

Although we are looking towards the centre of our Galaxy, the central bulge itself is obscured by opaque foreground dust clouds (see image on page 15). The clearest area is on the Sagittarius side of the Milky Way. The light we see there comes from 25 000 light years away, so we are seeing things as they were in 23 000 BC!

LOOKING THROUGH BINOCULARS

Try scanning with binoculars and you will sight numerous clusters great and small, dark dust clouds (seen in silhouette against the brighter background) and possibly glowing 'nebulae' (Latin for 'clouds'). The following objects can be located with the aid of the map on the opposite page.

GALACTIC CLUSTERS

Close to the scorpion's tail are Messier 6 and 7 (Charl Messier first listed them in the eighteenth century). The naked eye sees them as indistinct luminous patches, but binoculars will reveal tens of individual stars in each. Even so, we can see only their brightest members; each cluster contains hundreds if not thousands of stars, all formed more or less at the same time. (Chapter 4, page 29, explains how stars form in Orion: this is what Orion might look like tens of millions of years from now.) In time these clusters will disperse, seeding the Galaxy with their offspring. Messier 6 (below) is 1 600 light years away, but Messier 7 (below) only half that distance.

GLOBULAR CLUSTERS

Since they cluster around the centre of the galaxy, there are a number of globular clusters in this portion of the sky. However, if you have already had a look at Omega Centauri, near the Southern Cross (see page 22), you will have seen the best example by far. The clusters in this area of the sky are fainter. For example, Messier 4 is very close to the bright star Antares (see below far right). Binoculars will reveal it as a fuzzy ball, its stars still too faint to resolve.

LAGOON NEBULA

There are a number of glowing 'emission nebulae' in this part of the sky, but even with binoculars they are not particularly bright (unlike the Great Nebula in Orion). The best one to try for is the Lagoon Nebula. Use the map on the opposite page to find it. Look for the asterism in Sagittarius called the Milk Dipper; its 'handle' will point you in the right direction.

Messier 7

Chapter 7
Pegasus and nearby galaxies

This chapter leads you from our Galaxy to neighbouring 'cities of stars'. Pegasus is the last of the big five constellations to spot. Read this chapter from September to January. At other times of the year, Pegasus will not be visible in the evening sky.

FINDING PEGASUS

Knowing which direction is north would help, as Pegasus can be found over the northern horizon. The stars of Pegasus are not particularly bright, but what makes them distinct is that they form an almost perfect square. To get an idea of how big a square to look for, clench the fingers of one hand, leaving the thumb sticking out, and hold at arm's length; the length from thumb tip to little finger is roughly equivalent to the length of one side of the square. There is only one such square to be found amongst the brighter stars of the sky (see diagrams to the right and below).

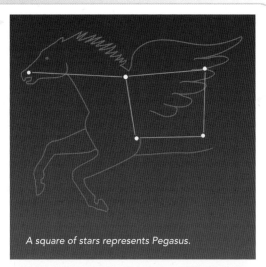
A square of stars represents Pegasus.

← WEST LOOKING NORTH EAST →

The visibility of Pegasus in the evening sky

PICTURES IN THE SKY
It takes the imagination of the ancient Greeks to turn a square into a winged horse. This constellation features in the story from Greek mythology, where Perseus, riding Pegasus, arrives just in time to rescue Andromeda – daughter of Cepheus and Cassiopeia – from a sea monster. The constellations of Cepheus and Cassiopeia lie in that small patch of sky not generally visible from southern Africa. Even Andromeda and Perseus never climb much above the horizon, but it is worth finding Andromeda for one important object.

THE GREAT GALAXY IN ANDROMEDA

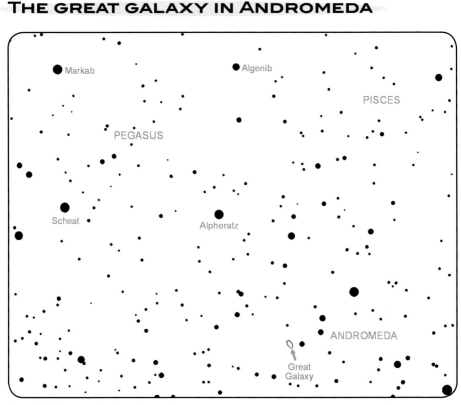

Markab

Algenib

PISCES

PEGASUS

Scheat

Alpheratz

ANDROMEDA

Great
Galaxy

Map of the Pegasus-Andromeda region

If you look at the map above, showing the Great Square of Pegasus, you will see that its bottom right-hand star is called Alpheratz. This is the start of a line of stars that heads down and to the right. Use the map to gauge where to look to find the Andromeda Galaxy. If it is not too low down on the horizon, you might just spot it with the naked eye. Looking through binoculars will reveal an elongated blur. Believe it or not, you are looking over two million light years out into space, and seeing this galaxy as it was two million years ago! Binoculars show only the central bulge of the galaxy (packed with billions of stars); were it possible to see the surrounding disc, the galaxy would appear far larger, some six times the diameter of the Moon.

The Andromeda Galaxy is a city of stars in itself, much like the galaxy in which we live, but slightly

The great galaxy in Andromeda

larger. Its spiral structure is similar to that of our own Galaxy (shown earlier in Chapter 2). From our perspective we see the Andromeda Galaxy almost edge on. The two giant spiral galaxies dominate a scattering of much smaller galaxies, collectively known as the Local Group. They are gradually being pulled towards each other, and will – in a few billion years time – start to merge. That will completely disrupt their spiral structures, but will not have any direct effect on individual solar systems such as ours.

THE MAGELLANIC CLOUDS

Of the other galaxies in the Local Group, only two small irregular galaxies, satellites to our Galaxy, are visible to the naked eye. If you have found the Great Square of Pegasus (over the northern horizon), then turn around and look in the opposite direction (over the southern horizon). On a good dark night, it should be possible to pick out two luminous clouds, like patches broken away from the Milky Way. Originally known to early European navigators as the 'Cape Clouds' (a reference to this part of the globe), they were renamed to honour Ferdinand Magellan. The lower one (at this time of year) is the Large Cloud.

THE LARGE MAGELLANIC CLOUD

This Galaxy is some 160 000 light years distant, so we will not be able to see its individual stars, even looking through binoculars. However, it is possible to pick out the Tarantula Nebula east of its centre. This is caused by ultraviolet light from a very compact cluster of hot stars exciting the gas around it. As such it is quite a unique object and, were it much closer, would outshine its counterparts in our Galaxy.

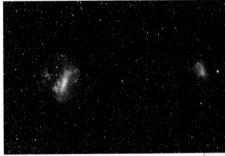

The Large and Small Magellanic Clouds

THE SMALL MAGELLANIC CLOUD

This Galaxy is 180 000 light years away, and it would require more than binoculars to bring out any detail. Right next to it, however – but very much in the foreground – is the globular cluster 47 Tucanae. This cluster is 13 400 light years distant, much too far away for individual stars to be seen; it resembles a fuzzy ball through binoculars (almost as spectacular a cluster as Omega Centauri on page 22, and better than Messier 4 on page 37).

THE LARGER UNIVERSE

Although it is possible that a few other galaxies, each city of stars separated from one another by perhaps a million or more light years, might be glimpsed as vague blurs through binoculars, they lie beyond naked-eye visibility and present a challenge outside the scope of this small book.

Suffice to say, the universe is populated by billions of galaxies, congregated in a labyrinth-like structure. Cosmological measurements suggest that in a universe estimated to be 13.7 billion years old, galaxies have been around for some 12 billion years. Consequently, using very powerful telescopes (like the Southern African Large Telescope in the Karoo), we can see 'back in time' to a distance of around 12 billion light years. Although close pairs of galaxies may be pulled together by their mutual gravity, in general the universe is expanding at an accelerating rate, carrying the galaxies further apart from one another.

CHAPTER 8
OTHER CREATURES IN THE NIGHT SKY

There are still quite a number of birds and animals in

the night sky that we have yet to spot. If you are a purist

and feel you must check off every one in the book, then

the rest of this chapter is for you. Unfortunately, even if you

were prepared to stay up all night, it is unlikely that every

last one of them will be visible on any given night; but

then that is the case with terrestrial animals as well!

About half of the 88 constellations recognised by the International Astronomical Union are named for animals, both wild and domestic. Of course, a number of the animal constellations have already been introduced in earlier chapters. Close to Orion we had Taurus the bull and Canis Major and Canis Minor, the large and small dogs. We also pointed out Leo the lion, Cancer the crab, and Scorpius the scorpion. Pegasus – the winged horse – is also an animal, but not one you are likely to spot in a game reserve today. Next to the Southern Cross and Scorpius are two centaurs – half human and half horse – that are more likely to be encountered in Harry Potter's Forbidden Forest than in Umfolozi. There is also a rich variety of bird life up above, by night as well as day. Soaring amongst the stars of the night sky are an eagle, a crane, a crow and a swan, to name only a few.

As mentioned previously, it was not only the Greek-Babylonian astronomers, but also the indigenous African people who identified the constellations with animals. The Belt of Orion was seen as three warthog or three zebra, the star Betelgeuse as a lion, the Southern Cross and Pointers as giraffes or lions. To the Khoisan, the stars were people and animals of an earlier generation.

Here is a number of birds and animals in the night sky that we have not yet tracked down. Choose the section (or sections) below according to the time of year. Just a word of caution: we have already covered the easy-to-recognise constellations. Almost all those listed in this chapter present a challenge.

SUMMER GAME VIEWING

If you haven't yet found Orion, go back and work through Chapter 4. The map on the next page shows some of the constellations in the neighbourhood of Orion.

Aries, the ram, is a constellation of the Zodiac. The Sun passes in front of it from late April to early May. If you have already discovered how to 'travel' from Orion to Taurus, then moving along a little further will bring you to Aries. The brightest star, Hamal, and its two companions form a trio, which is not particularly easy to identify. Hamal is 66 light years distant.

Lepus, the hare, crouches – possibly for protection from Taurus – at Orion's feet. Since we see Orion upside down from the Southern Hemisphere, you generally need to look immediately above Orion to pick out the asterism representing Lepus. The stars of Lepus are relatively bright, but their irregular pattern – vaguely diamond shaped – is difficult to recognise.

Columba, the dove, is also composed of a distinctive asterism. Its two brightest stars make a distinct pair. You can find it by going from Orion to Lepus, then continuing in the same direction.

Monoceros is the constellation found in a stretch of the Milky Way alongside Orion that lacks any bright stars. If you succeeded in finding Canis Major and Canis Minor – on either side of the Milky way – Monoceros is in the almost blank bit of sky between them. It takes a moment to recognise what animal the Latin word refers to. The answer is another animal you will struggle to find in the Kruger (a unicorn).

Eridanus is not an animal, but still something likely to be found in a game reserve; it is a river. In the sky it is a large, sprawling constellation – a meandering line of stars – to the left of Orion and Lepus, with an extension southwestwards eventually leading to the bright star Achernar (which is 144 light years distant).

Cetus is not an animal likely to be found in game reserves, but our southern coasts do play host to the migrations of whales. Whether the one in the sky is a Southern Right or Humpback is unclear, but the constellation of Cetus covers a large tract of sky just above Aries. Save for

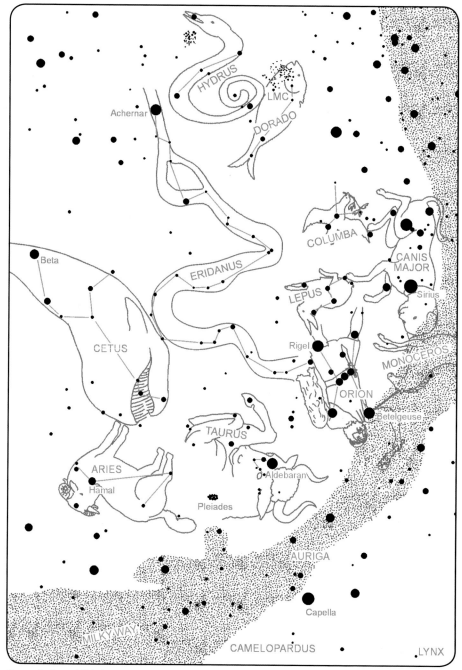

Constellations visible in summer

the isolated star, Beta Ceti, it has only a scattering of fainter stars, with few, if any, distinctive asterisms to aid recognition.

Hydrus to the south, close to where Eridanus begins, is a sea serpent. Its three brightest stars are widely spaced, and one is a companion to the bright star Achernar in Eridanus.

Dorado, the fish, just below Hydrus, is a fairly inconspicuous southern constellation. It has a weak line of stars leading from the Large Magellanic Cloud (see also page 41).

Camelopardus, the giraffe, is so far north that it is difficult to see it from the latitudes of southern Africa. This is a rather indistinct constellation, little more than a scattering of faint stars, most of which would almost certainly be very low, if not below the northern horizon. If you earlier found Auriga, as detailed in Chapter 4, Camelopardus is the constellation immediately below it.

AUTUMN GAME VIEWING

The Southern Cross (Chapter 3) and Leo (Chapter 5) are visible during autumn evenings. Once you have located them and their associated constellations, you can move on to the constellations listed below. Some have quite distinctive star patterns, while others merely 'fill in the open spaces'.

Corvus, the crow, can be found halfway between the tail of Leo and the Cross. It is a distinct asterism of five reasonably bright stars. During May evenings, it will be virtually overhead.

Hydra, the mythical water snake or sea monster, is a large, sprawling constellation. A few stars mark its head, not far from Leo's front paws, and there is a single bright star – Alpha Hydrae – further down its body. Its tail brushes Corvus on the Southern Cross side .

Ursa Major, the big bear, is one of the best-known constellations of the Northern Hemisphere. From southern Africa it is visible very low on the horizon, when Leo is relatively high in the sky. In the southernmost parts (around the latitude of Port Elizabeth or Cape Town), much of it will be just below the horizon, or lost in the haze. Every degree of latitude north helps; in the Kruger it will be visible just above the horizon and in Namibia, Botswana and Zimbabwe it will be situated well above the horizon. Ursa Major contains a distinctive asterism known as the 'Big Dipper' (in the USA), the 'Plough' (in Britain) or the 'Wagon' (in Germany). From the Southern Hemisphere the Big Dipper appears upside down, with the 'bowl' of the spoon inverted to the left, and the 'handle' to the right.

Leo Minor, the lion cub, is found below the sickle-shaped asterism that forms the 'head' of Leo. It has only faint stars.

Lynx is situated down and to the left of the sickle in Leo. It is a very faint constellation that lies beneath the equally indistinct constellation of Cancer.

Canes Venatici, the two hunting dogs, lies between the 'tail' of Leo and the handle of the Big Dipper. It is little more than a triangle of faint stars.

IN THE KAROO
'Trek-bokke' – Springbok – once migrated in tens of thousands across the harsh landscape of the Karoo. Today only pockets of indigenous fauna remain, one of which is the site of the South African Astronomical Observatory near Sutherland. Here telescopes cluster on a high plateau. At night – as in game reserves – artificial light is absent or hidden.

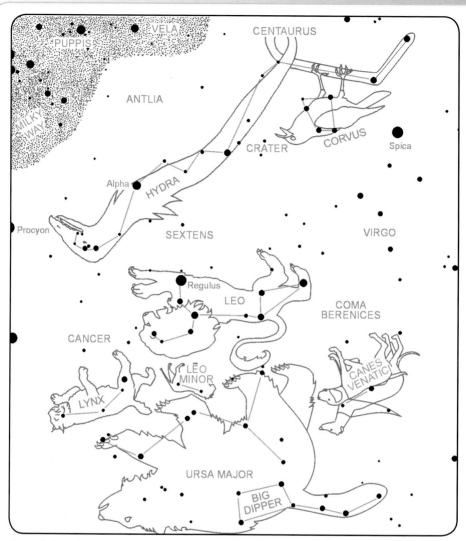

Constellations visible in autumn

WINTER GAME VIEWING

The Milky Way in winter is a wonderful sight. Scorpius and Sagittarius (*see* Chapter 6) lie across it, towards the centre. This is a good starting point from which to locate the following less obvious constellations. Begin by following the line of the Milky Way towards the north.

Aquila, the eagle, is an appropriate constellation to find high in the sky above a game park. It is relatively easy to spot as it is dominated by Altair, one of the brightest stars in the sky. Altair, only 17 light years distant, is easy to identify as it has two companion stars, one on either side. However, it requires some imagination to picture a soaring eagle!

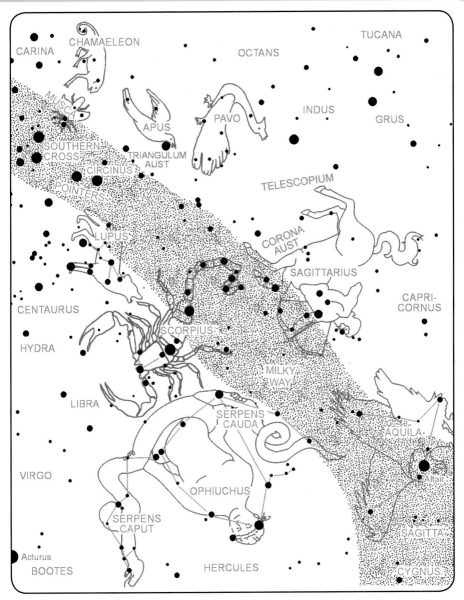

Constellations visible in winter

Lupus, the wolf, can be found by following the Milky Way in the other direction, towards the Southern Cross. Its star patterns lend themselves to acquired recognition. It is a neighbour of Scorpius, and is located on the same side of the Milky Way. Its star pattern hardly resembles a wolf and, situated so far south, it is somewhat misplaced, from a geographic point of view.

Musca, the fly, is a small constellation bordering the Southern Cross, and in line with the Cross's main axis. Its compact asterism, including a distinct pair of stars, makes it easy to identify.

Chamaeleon is a modest constellation, the next after Musca. It can be found by following the line of the Cross's main axis.

Apus, the bird of paradise, has only faint stars. It is situated next to Triangulum Australe, the distinctive triangle near the Pointers of the Southern Cross.

Pavo, the peacock, is similarly exotic but far from conspicuous. Pavo lies off the 'point' of Triangulum Australe.

Serpens Caput and **Serpens Cauda**, both snakes, are two indistinct constellations that, appropriately enough, are difficult to spot. Ophiuchus, the doctor of antiquity, is depicted wrestling with them (the serpent is still used as a symbol of medicine today). The map on the previous page will guide you in finding them. Look for the almost straight line of stars located below Scorpius. One end of it is Serpens Caput, the other leads to Serpens Cauda.

SPRING GAME VIEWING

Almost all the easily recognisable constellations are either low on, or below, the horizon. The exception is the Great Square of Pegasus (Chaprer Seven). Use it as a central reference point to find a great variety of bird and animal constellations.

Cygnus, the swan, can be found by following the Milky Way all the way to the northern horizon. Look out for the bright star, Deneb. It forms the tail of an elegant swan in flight with its wings outstretched. It is sometimes referred to it as the Northern Cross, though its stars are nowhere near as bright, and its pattern not as compact, as the Southern Cross.

Delphinus, a compact asterism that includes a diamond shape, is situated not far above Cygnus. It represents a dolphin.

Vulpecula, which is supposedly a fox catching a goose, is depicted by several very faint stars between Cygnus and Delphinus.

Pisces may be a well-known constellation of the Zodiac, but the pair of fish can be discerned only as a large but very indistinct splattering of stars above and to the right of Pegasus.

Piscis Australis, another fish constellation, is located further south. Look for a bright star well above Pegasus. It is Fomalhaut, a relatively nearby star 25 light years away and the brightest member of this otherwise unremarkable constellation.

Grus, another appropriate constellation to be viewed from a game reserve, is supposed to represent a crane in flight. It is situated not too far from Fomalhaut. Its pattern forms a long triangle and it has two pairs of double stars that make it easily recognisable.

Phoenix, the mythological bird capable of rising again from its ashes, has reasonably bright stars. It lies more or less between the bright stars Fomalhaut and Achernar.

Tucana is a fainter constellation that can be found directly beyond Grus and Phoenix. The toucan completes this trio of birds.

Capricornus is one of the constellations of the Zodiac (the Sun appears to pass through it from late January to early February). It has a scattering of stars, but is fairly difficult to locate. Capricornus represents the god Pan, who desperately tried to change himself into a fish to escape the demon Typhon, but only half succeeded. The result was a bizarre creature, half goat, half fish.

Hardly game reserve material!

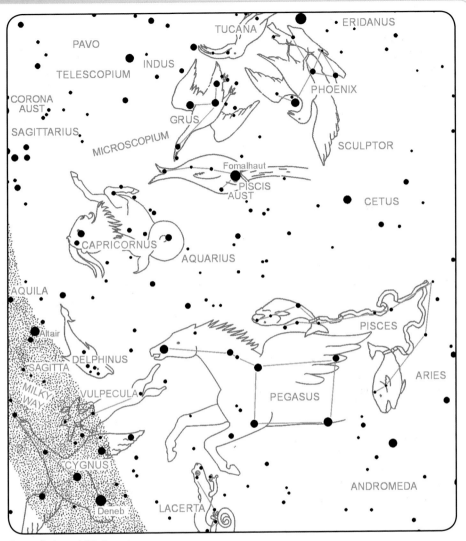

Constellations visible in spring

SALT

The South African Astronomical Observatory is home to the largest aperture telescope in the Southern Hemisphere. Capable of detecting the light of a candle at the distance of the Moon, the Southern African Large Telescope (SALT) was inaugurated in 2005. It can peer deep into space and billions of years back into time.

CHAPTER 9
TRACKING THE PLANETS

You may encounter occasional bright 'stars' that do
not feature in the maps in this book. These objects are almost
certainly planets – Mercury, Venus, Mars, Jupiter or Saturn – that
are sufficiently distant so as not to appear as discs, like the Moon,
to the naked eye. Instead they resemble bright stars. They meander
slowly against the starry backdrop, keeping to that band of sky
known as the Zodiac (which includes Aries, Taurus, Gemini,
Cancer, Leo, Scorpius, Sagittarius, Capricornus and Pisces).

WHICH PLANET IS WHICH?

Keeping track of the movements of the planets is a complex affair because these movements reflect both the planets' own motions and the motion of our Earth. All the planets are moving around the Sun together, but every now and then Mercury and Venus overtake Earth, and Earth in turn overtakes Mars, Jupiter and Saturn. The arrangement of planets in the night sky is different from week to week, month to month and year to year, so there is no easy way to determine which ones are visible at a particular time of the year, or time of the night. Fortunately, it is not too difficult to determine which planet is which:

- If it is incredibly bright and white, it's Venus. Venus can be seen in the west in the evening or in the east before sunrise, but never late at night.
- If it is very bright – brighter than any star (but shines with a steady yellow light), it's Jupiter.
- If it has a reddish tinge and ranges from being very bright to relatively faint, it's Mars.
- If it is yellowish and just as bright as the brightest stars, it's Saturn.
- If it resembles a reasonably bright star seen low in the west in the early evening, or low in the east before sunrise, it's Mercury.

VENUS

Venus is the third brightest object in the sky (after the Sun and Moon). At times it is bright enough to be visible in the daytime to the naked eye! It is probably responsible for 99% of the phone calls to observatories and planetariums reporting an amazingly bright object in the sky. It also accounts for most UFO sightings.

Venus appears so incredibly bright because it is completely covered by white cloud; it is also closer to the Sun, and comes closer to the Earth than any other planet. It takes seven months to go around the Sun, as opposed to the 12 months it takes Earth. This means that Venus overtakes Earth once every 19 months. So, in terms of visibility, it goes through a 19-month cycle. For half that time it is 'catching up' with Earth and appears in the evening sky, above the western horizon. For the other half of the cycle it is leaving us behind and appears in the early morning sky above the eastern horizon. The only time

A global view of the surface of Venus revealed by radar mapping through its dense white clouds.

we will not be able to see it is when it is lost in the Sun's glare, either going around the far side or passing between the Sun and Earth (as it overtakes us). Its brightness peaks about a month before and after overtaking. The reason it does not get brighter as it gets very close is that by that time its night-side hemisphere is facing our way (see image below). For a month or two before and after it overtakes us, it is close enough and big enough that its crescent phase may be visible through binoculars (provided one can steady them by resting the elbows on something solid).

The phases of Venus

Venus is well known to the indigenous people of Southern Africa. When seen in the early morning (*Ikhwezi lokusa* in Xhosa), it is associated with diligence (a time to start daily chores). When seen in the early evening (*uCelizapholo*) it is linked to the milking of cows.

Although almost the size of Earth, Venus is probably the most unlikely place in the solar system for any form of life as we know it to survive. Beneath the white clouds, its thick carbon dioxide atmosphere traps the penetrating heat. It is a greenhouse gone wrong, and a good reason for us to worry about global warming on Earth. Its surface temperature is around 500 degrees Celsius! In addition, surface pressure is ninety times that of the Earth, so in that regard it would be like trying to visit the Titanic on the bottom of the sea.

SEEING VENUS BY DAY

If you have gone on game drives around sunrise or sunset in clear weather, there is a good chance you will have spotted Venus. You should therefore have a reasonable idea of its position in the sky relative to the Sun; it is of course never very far from the Sun. When the Sun is a bit above the horizon, Venus will be in roughly the same place, but a bit higher. Search for it with binoculars (but be very careful never to aim your binoculars at the Sun); it is not difficult to find. You will then have the pleasure of seeing it against the blue daytime sky. Once you know exactly where to look, try shifting your position to get a branch of a tree as a marker, then look with the naked eye. If Venus is bright enough, and if its image falls on the central spot of your eye, you will be surprised to find that you can see it clearly. You may also try finding it at midday, remembering once again never to look at the Sun through binoculars. Those with very sharp eyesight can find it without binoculars, but binoculars make the job so much easier.

JUPITER

It takes Jupiter almost 12 years to go around the Sun, causing it to go through a thirteen-month cycle of visibility. It is visible in the evening sky for about six months of its cycle. It is the fourth brightest object in the sky – after the Sun, Moon and Venus – and brighter than any night-time

Jupiter and its moons

star, so it is easy to recognise with the naked eye. You should also try looking at it with binoculars; remember to steady them by resting your elbows on a firm surface. Binoculars will just reveal the disc of Jupiter, though without enough magnification to reveal any detail. However, they will show a line of four moons – like tiny stars – accompanying Jupiter. These are the Galilean moons: Europa, Io, Ganymede and Callisto. Galileo Galilei was the first person to discover them with a telescope not much better than modern binoculars. The configurations of the moons change from night to night as they orbit their massive host.

Jupiter is the king of the Solar System; more massive than all the other planets put together, it is 11 times the diameter and 300 times the mass of Earth. A telescope pointed toward Jupiter reveals bands and spots in its cloudy atmosphere. Beneath those clouds there is no solid surface, for the bulk of the planet is liquid hydrogen with a core of heavy elements.

The Xhosa people sometimes associated Jupiter with night-time travel, as it was often visible for much of the night, and somehow seemed to guide the traveller.

MARS

Mars revolves around the Sun in a period of 23 months. Once every 25 months, the Earth over-takes Mars, and while the two planets are close to each other, Mars is very bright, about on par with Jupiter. Its brightness is not sustained, however, and generally it is a fairly inconspicuous object; the faintest of the planets when it is furthest from Earth. Yet identifying it is fairly easy because of its distinctive orange colour.

The Earth will overtake Mars on the following dates over the next 15 years: December 2007, January 2010, March 2012, April 2014, May 2016, July 2018 and October 2020. For a few months before these dates, until a few months after, Mars will be bright and conspicuous, some-where over the eastern horizon in the evening sky.

Smaller than the Earth, Mars gets its distinctive colour from its desert sands. The Mars Rovers that landed so successfully in January 2004 appeared to have been put down in the Namib or the

Sahara, judging from the pictures of sandy expanses and wind-scoured ridges they sent back. The most exciting information to come from the Rovers was the discovery that, at some point in its past, Mars was a much wetter place with flowing water. The big question is whether microscopic life (possibly seeded from Earth) could ever have taken root there. Mars is, without a doubt, the planet that most closely resembles Earth, except for the obvious absence of flora and fauna. However, it is only half the diameter of our home planet. Even at its closest, its disc is not large enough to be seen through binoculars.

Mars as seen through the Hubble telescope

SATURN

The famous ringed planet takes 29 years to circle the Sun, apparently oscillating forward and backward as it does so; this oscillation, however, is caused by the Earth's motion and the fact that Saturn moves so slowly. Saturn will be seen against the constellation of Cancer during 2005-2006, against Leo during 2007-2009, against Virgo during 2010-2013, against Libra during 2014-2015 and it will reach Scorpius in 2016 and Sagittarius by 2018-2020.

The angle of the rings of Saturn changes over time.

Saturn looks like a bright star but shines with a steady yellowish light. Of course everybody yearns to see its rings, but unfortunately that requires a good telescope; binoculars are not up to the job. However, you might just glimpse its large moon, Titan, close to the planet. Nine times the diameter of Earth, Saturn is a smaller version of Jupiter. It, too, is mainly composed of liquid hydrogen, with gaseous outer layers and heavy elements in a dense core.

The average density of Saturn is low enough for it to float in water, were that possible. It is famous for its rings but they are hardly unique; Jupiter, Uranus and Neptune also have rings (although those of Jupiter are barely detectable). The Cassini spacecraft, which went into orbit around Saturn in June 2004, has sent us a wealth of close-up pictures, especially those showing detailed structures in the ring and the cratered surfaces of its many smaller moons.

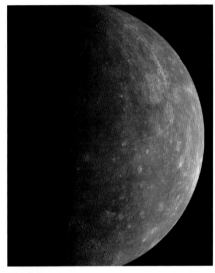

The Huygens spacecraft, which rode piggyback and then separated from the mother craft, descended through the cloudy atmosphere of Titan and gave us our first clear look at its surface, revealing apparently dried lakes and rivers. Since the planet is far too cold for liquid water, the rivers and lakes may have been formed by liquid methane.

MERCURY

Because it is so close to the Sun, Mercury – although relatively bright – is the most difficult planet to spot. During evening twilight it may appear low on the western horizon, setting early. Alternatively, in morning twilight it may rise in the east just ahead of the Sun. More often than not, it is lost in the glare of the Sun. It goes around the Sun in three months and has a four-month visibility cycle.

Mercury

Our close-up views of Mercury are limited to the Mariner spacecraft photography made in the 1970s. Currently the Messenger spacecraft is *en route*, expecting to go into orbit about the planet in 2011.

URANUS & NEPTUNE

Uranus sits on the borderline of naked-eye visibility, and can be viewed through binoculars, but you would need special charts (such as those given in *Sky Guide Africa South*) to find it.

Neptune, the last of the other eight major planets in our solar system, can only be located with a telescope.

Uranus close up

CHAPTER 10
STAR MAPS

This book has featured many star maps of individual constellations, or groups of constellations, but those maps only cover portions of the night sky. By contrast, this final chapter has a set of maps that covers the entire sky visible from southern Africa. However, only the brighter stars are shown, the representations of constellations are much smaller, and details shown earlier are absent.

This chapter contains 12 maps (one for each month of the year), each depicting the evening sky around 20h00 to 21h00. The maps reveal the gradual progression of constellations from the eastern to the western horizon, except in the very south, where a portion of the sky spins around the celestial pole, but does not set. The maps can also depict other times of the night when used in conjunction with a table (see below). For example, Map 1, which shows the evening sky in January, can equally well be used at 05h00 in the morning in September.

HOW TO USE THE MAPS

The cardinal points on the map – north, south, east and west – are not the same way round as they would be on a normal geographic map. On astronomical maps, if north is up, then east is to the left! This is because, on geographical maps, the viewer is looking *down*, whereas, in astronomy, the viewer is looking *up*. Hold one of these maps above your head and you will be able to align the cardinal points correctly. The sky is represented in such a way that *the centre of the map is directly overhead*. Holding a map above your head is hardly very comfortable, however. Instead, hold the map vertically in front of you and rotate it to match the direction in which you are looking. The printing on the maps will help you to orient yourself. For instance, if you are looking south, rotate the map through 180 degrees so the words 'Looking south' are upright. Then you will be able to make out which constellations are above the southern horizon.

Depending on your location, constellations might appear a little higher or lower over the northern and southern horizons (the maps are set for a latitude of 30 degrees south). Likewise, depending on the exact time, constellations over the eastern and western horizons may appear a little higher or lower. Remember that the maps compress the entire visible night sky – horizon to horizon – into the confines of a small, circular picture. Consequently, things appear much smaller on the map than they are in the night sky. The maps do not show the moon or planets.

	19h	21h	23h	01h	03h	05h
Jan	12	1	2	3	4	5
Feb	1	2	3	4	5	6
Mar	2	3	4	5	6	7
Apr	3	4	5	6	7	8
May	4	5	6	7	8	9
Jun	5	6	7	8	9	10
Jul	6	7	8	9	10	11
Aug	7	8	9	10	11	12
Sep	8	9	10	11	12	1
Oct	9	10	11	12	1	2
Nov	10	11	12	1	2	3
Dec	11	12	1	2	3	4

Which map should you use at different times of the night? The maps depict the night sky from about 8:00 to 9:00 pm around the middle of each month. Refer to this table to determine which map to use at any other time of the night. Numbers refer to star map numbers.

MAP 1
MID-JANUARY ABOUT 21:00

Mid-February about 19:00   Mid-December about 23:00

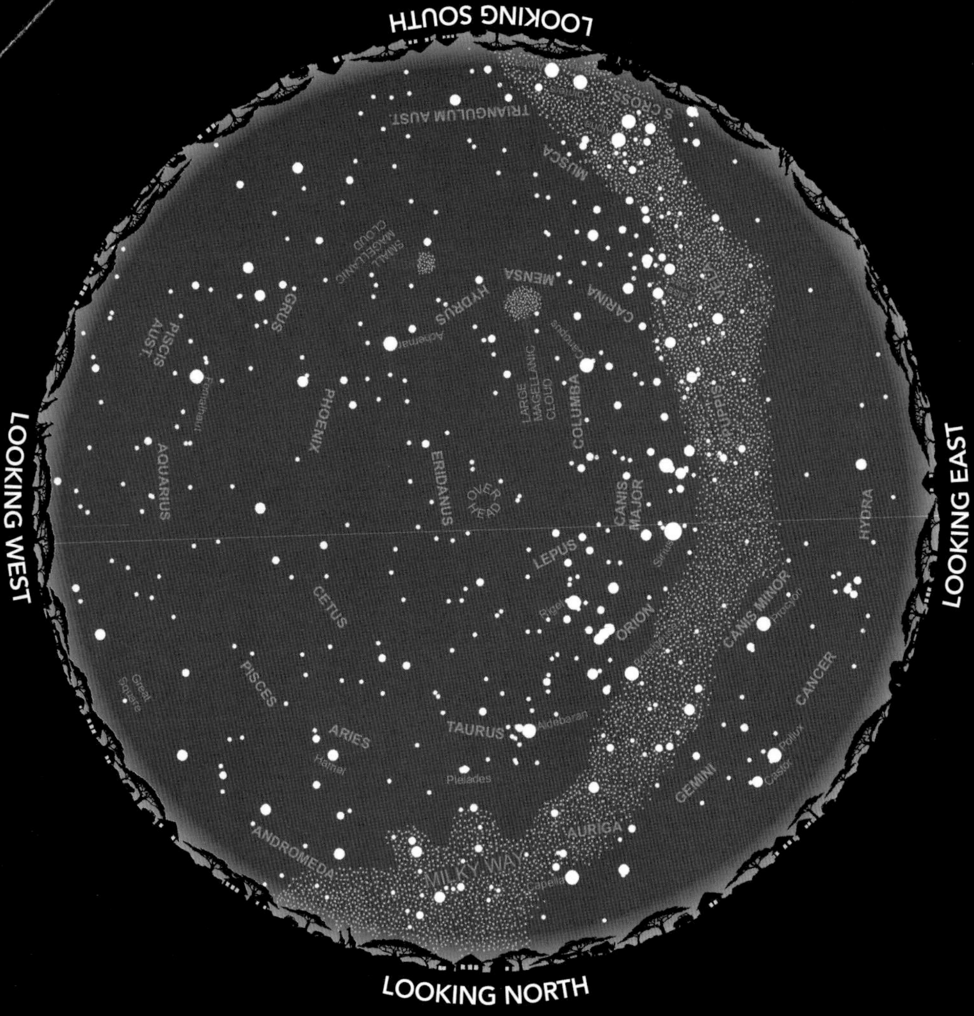

LOOKING SOUTH

LOOKING WEST

LOOKING EAST

TRIANGULUM AUST.

MUSCA

MENSA

CARINA

HYDRUS

SMALL MAGELLANIC CLOUD

GRUS

PISCIS AUST.

PHOENIX

COLUMBA

LARGE MAGELLANIC CLOUD

Achernar

VELA

PUPPIS

AQUARIUS

ERIDANUS

OVER HEAD

CANIS MAJOR

Sirius

HYDRA

CETUS

LEPUS

CANIS MINOR

Procyon

PISCES

ORION

CANCER

Great Square

ARIES

TAURUS

Aldebaran

GEMINI

Castor

Pollux

Hamal

Pleiades

AURIGA

ANDROMEDA

MILKY WAY

LOOKING NORTH

Hold the map up in front of you and rotate to match the direction in which you are looking.

Orion (Chapter 4) is prominent above the north-eastern horizon. The Southern Cross and Pointers (Chapter 3) are just beginning to rise above the southern horizon.

Orion (Chapter 4) is at its highest, above the northern horizon. The Southern Cross (Chapter 3) lies on its side above the south-eastern horizon, with the Pointers below it. Leo (Chapter 5) is just rising in the north-east.

Do not lay flat on a table, or the points of a compass will be the wrong way round.

MAP 3
MID-MARCH ABOUT 21:00

Mid-April about 19:00   Mid-February about 23:00

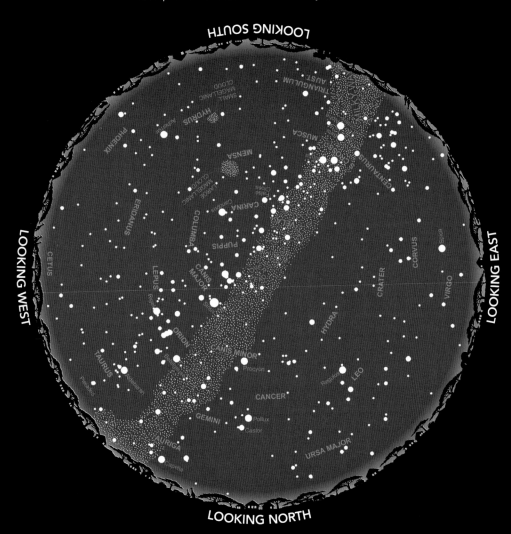

LOOKING SOUTH

LOOKING WEST

LOOKING EAST

LOOKING NORTH

Hold the map up in front of you and rotate to match the direction in which you are looking.

Orion (Chapter 4) is high above the north-western horizon, while Leo (Chapter 5) is rising in the north east. The Southern Cross (Chapter 3) lies on its side above the south-eastern horizon, with the Pointers below it.

MAP 4
MID-APRIL ABOUT 21:00

Mid-May about 19:00   *Mid-March about 23:00*

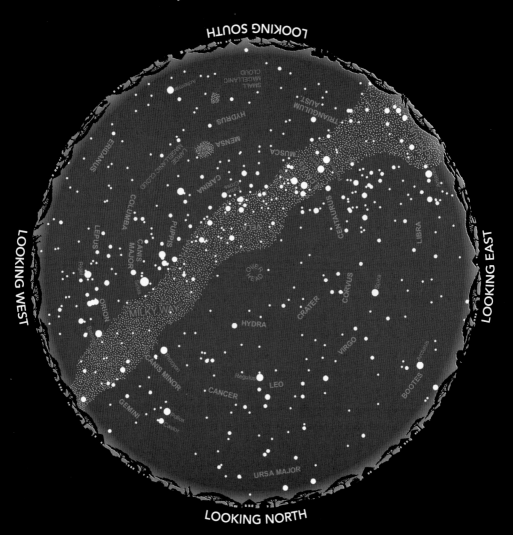

LOOKING SOUTH

LOOKING WEST

LOOKING EAST

LOOKING NORTH

Orion (Chapter 4) is low in the west, but Leo (Chapter 5) is high in the north. The Southern Cross and Pointers (Chapter 3) are climbing high in the south. Scorpius (Chapter 6) is rising in the east.

Do not lay flat on a table, or the points of a compass will be the wrong way round.

MAP 5
MID-MAY ABOUT 21:00

Mid-June about 19:00   Mid-April about 23:00

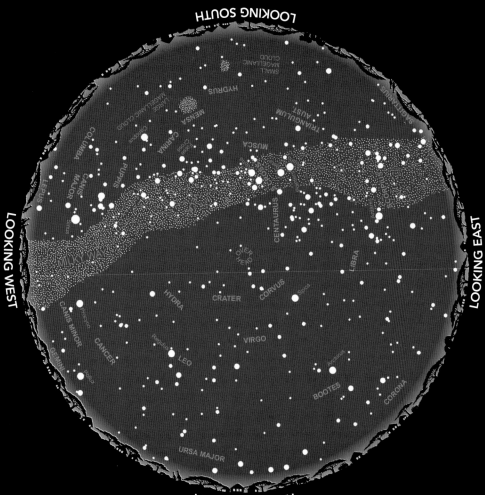

LOOKING SOUTH

LOOKING WEST

LOOKING EAST

LOOKING NORTH

Hold the map up in front of you and rotate to match the direction in which you are looking.

Leo (Chapter 5) is high in the north, while Scorpius (Chapter 6) is rising in the east. The Southern Cross (Chapter 3) stands almost upright, very high in the south.

LOOKING SOUTH

LOOKING EAST

LOOKING WEST

MILKY WAY

GRUS
SMALL MAGELLANIC CLOUD
LARGE MAGELLANIC CLOUD
HYDRUS
MENSA
CARINA
PUPPIS
CANIS MAJOR
MUSCA
CROSS
TRIANGULUM AUST.
SAGITTARIUS
CAPRICORNUS
CENTAURUS
LIBRA
HYDRA
CRATER
CORVUS
VIRGO
Spica
LEO
Arcturus
BOOTES
HERCULES
CORONA
URSA MAJOR

LOOKING NORTH

Scorpius (Chapter 6) stands high above the eastern horizon. Leo (Chapter 5) is low in the north-west. The Southern Cross (Chapter 3), almost upright, is very high above the southern horizon.

Do not lay flat on a table, or the points of a compass will be the wrong way round.

STAR MAP 6 **63**

LOOKING SOUTH

LARGE MAGELLANIC CLOUD

HYDRUS

MENSA

CARINA

VELA

MUSCA

CROSS

CENTAURUS

TRIANGULUM AUST.

SMALL MAGELLANIC CLOUD

GRUS

PISCIS AUST.

HYDRA

CRATER

CORVUS

Spica

LIBRA

SCORPIUS

SAGITTARIUS

CAPRICORNUS

MILKY WAY

VIRGO

LEO

AQUILA

BOOTES

Arcturus

CORONA

LYRA

HERCULES

Vega

LOOKING NORTH

LOOKING WEST

LOOKING EAST

Hold the map up in front of you and rotate to match the direction in which you are looking.

Scorpius (Chapter 6) is high overhead. The Southern Cross (Chapter 3) is high above the south-western horizon with the Pointers above it.

MAP 8
MID-AUGUST ABOUT 21:00

Mid-September about 19:00   *Mid-July about 23:00*

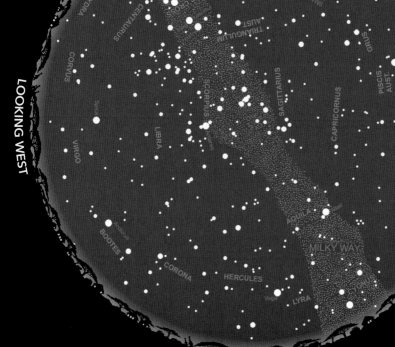

LOOKING SOUTH

LOOKING WEST

LOOKING EAST

LOOKING NORTH

Scorpius (Chapter 6) is just west of overhead. The Southern Cross (Chapter 3) lies on its side above the south-western horizon, with the Pointers above it.

Do not lay flat on a table, or the points of a compass will be the wrong way round.

Map 9
Mid-September about 21:00

Mid-October about 19:00   *Mid-August about 23:00*

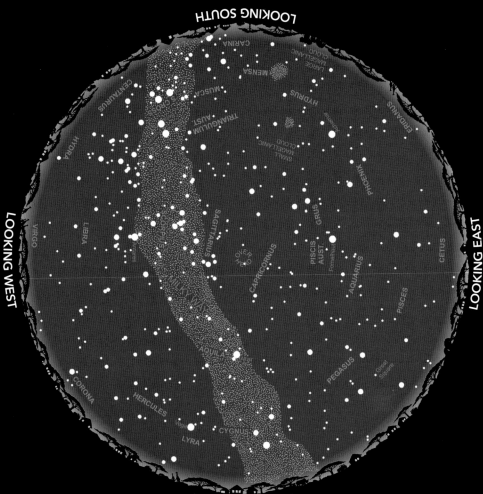

LOOKING SOUTH

LOOKING WEST

LOOKING EAST

LOOKING NORTH

Hold the map up in front of you and rotate to match the direction in which you are looking.

Scorpius (Chapter 6) is high over the western horizon. The Southern Cross (Chapter 3) – on its side with the Pointers above it – is low in the south-west. In the north-east, Pegasus (Chapter 7) is rising.

MAP 10
MID-OCTOBER ABOUT 21:00

Mid-November about 19:00   Mid-September about 23:00

LOOKING SOUTH

LOOKING WEST

LOOKING EAST

LOOKING NORTH

Scorpius (Chapter 6) is above the western horizon, while Pegasus (Chapter 7) is well above the northern horizon.

Do not lay flat on a table, or the points of a compass will be the wrong way round.

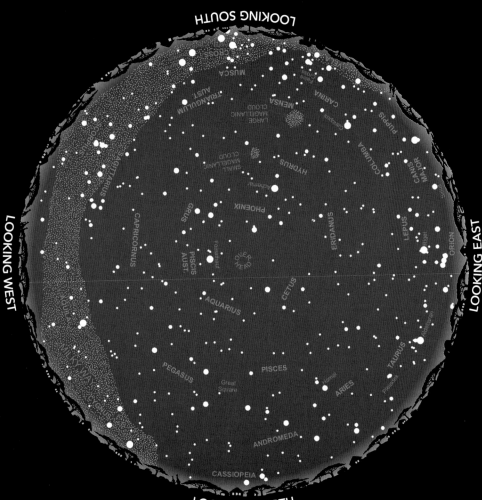

LOOKING SOUTH

LOOKING WEST

LOOKING EAST

LOOKING NORTH

Hold the map up in front of you and rotate to match the direction in which you are looking.

Pegasus (Chapter 7) is high over the northern horizon while Orion (Chapter 4) is just rising in the east.

Map 12
Mid-December about 21:00

Mid-November about 19:00   Mid-January about 23:00

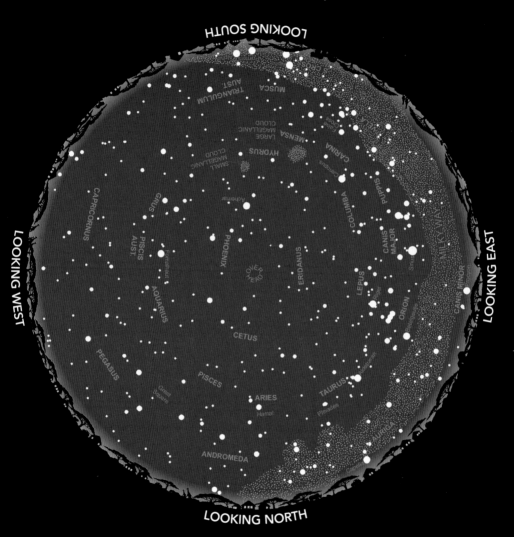

LOOKING SOUTH

LOOKING WEST

LOOKING EAST

LOOKING NORTH

Orion (Chapter 4) is well above the eastern horizon, while Pegasus (Chapter 7) is over the north-western horizon.

Do not lay flat on a table, or the points of a compass will be the wrong way round.

Glossary

Asterism: A distinctive, compact pattern of stars (not as large as a constellation).

Averted vision: The type of vision wherein the eye can perceive very faint objects by looking a little to the side of the faint objects.

Cone receptors: Light receptors in the retina of the eye employed for daytime vision.

Constellation: Region of the night sky that usually contains a distinctive pattern of stars, named for some imaginary creature or object.

Galactic cluster: Cluster of hundreds of stars (only some of which are bright enough to be visible).

Galaxy: The gigantic disc-shaped stellar system in which our Sun is situated; one of billions in the observable Universe.

Globular cluster: Distant cluster of hundreds of thousands of stars that looks like a fuzzy ball through binoculars.

Interstellar gas: Gas clouds, usually very tenuous, between the stars.

Intertropical Convergence Zone: Band of tropical cloud (esp. thunderstorms) that migrates north and south of the Earth's equator with the seasons.

Milky Way: The visible portion of our Galaxy that forms an encircling band.

Nebula: Latin word for 'cloud' usually applied to glowing clouds of interstellar gas.

Planet: A body, in orbit around our Sun or other stars, that shines by reflected light.

Red giant: An enormous, swollen star. A brief episode in the life of a star before it dies.

Rod receptors: Light receptors in the retina of the eye, used for night vision.

Satellites: Anything that orbits a larger body, usually artificial objects around the Earth.

Star: A large incandescent spherical body, like our Sun, powered by nuclear fusion.

White dwarf: Final dense state of the core of a dying star.

Zodiac: The encircling band of constellations, against which the Sun and planets appear to move.

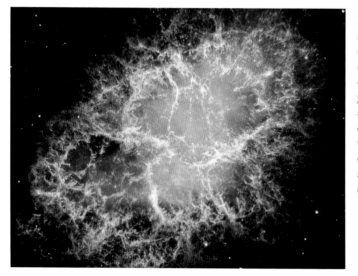

The Crab Nebula is the remnant of the outer layers of a once massive star seen to explode some 950 years ago. Only huge stars are believed to end their lives in this way and, happily, since our Sun is comparatively small, it will not end up like the Crab Nebubla.

INDEX